PREHISTORIC ANIMALS

*

DR. JOSEPH AUGUSTA
Professor of Paleontology

Illustrated under the direction of the author by
ZDENĚK BURIAN

Translated by Dr. Greta Hort

*

PAUL HAMLYN • LONDON

First published 1960

Second impression 1961

Third impression 1962

Fourth impression 1964

Fifth impression 1967

Designed and produced by
ARTIA
for
PAUL HAMLYN LTD
DRURY HOUSE • RUSSELL STREET • LONDON

Printed in Czechoslovakia by Polygrafia Prague
S-2145

CONTENTS

LIST OF PLATES

INTRODUCTION

The Earth, which is said to be a speck of dust in the infinite spaces of the universe and an obedient planet ceaselessly circling round the Sun, is the cradle and grave of all the creation whose life is tied to it. From the time that life first appeared on the Earth, birth, development, old age and death follow upon each other in a never-broken succession. The Earth, that speck of dust, is the cradle and grave of all living things.

From the very beginning of the history of life on Earth we see how life constantly develops and progresses, how it is constantly being enriched by new, ever higher and more complex forms, how even man, the culmination of all living things on the Earth, is tied to it by his life. It is his cradle and grave also. But man would not be man if he did not try to know the primeval history of his Earth, if he did not try to discover what changes it has undergone in the course of long geological ages, if he did not try to find out how life originated, how it developed, what laws govern its evolution, if he did not try to obtain an answer to the question of the when and how of his own origin. And so geologists and paleontologists arose who devoted all their efforts and even the whole of their life to the study of the history of the Earth and its creatures. The geologists delved into the Earth to learn its history, while the paleontologists studied the history of the life which pulsates on it today as in ages past.

What libraries and archives, with their books and ancient chronicles and records on yellowed parchment, are to the historian, nature herself is to the paleontologist; only his books and parchments are the mossy rocks, the underground caverns, the steep walls of sand- and loampits, of the quarries and river beds of nature. Laboriously he uncovers fossil after fossil, carefully he guards them and keeps them for further study in collections, for each fossil freed from its rock tomb is a precious document of life in ancient geological ages. Each fossil is to the paleontologist a tiny letter in a vast alphabet, but patiently he collects and arranges these tiny letters until they form words and the words sentences, which then tell him a little of the ancient history of the life of our world. For more than 150 years the paleontologists of all countries and of all nations have attempted thus to compile and read the ancient history of life on our Earth. They do not shun fatigue and hardship, discomfort and privation when their desire for knowledge drags them into inhospitable northern regions with cruel frosts, icy winds and permanently frozen soil, or into sandy wastes and stony deserts scorched by the pitiless rays of the sun. They climb the peaks of the highest mountains with the same undaunted courage with which they descend the walls of the deepest canyons, there to extract the fossils which will complete one more word, one more sentence for them in the vast book of the history of life.

Already a long time ago paleontologists ceased to be content with merely labelling and describing the fossils they found. The central question for the modern paleontologist is the question of evolution; it is his aim to discover the phylogenetic evolution of all living things, to ascertain how each phylum with all its branches arose in the course of the geological ages, how it developed, reached its time of maximum expansion, and then degenerated, even sometimes dying out completely, and to search for the causes and laws of this evolution and its phases. All the strivings of modern paleon-

tologists are bent towards this one goal, and in many ways their work also has far-reaching consequences for the understanding of the life of today.

Though it has been known already for a long time that the organisms of the different geological periods were different, yet it was for long believed that all living things had been created in their present form and did not change. The famous work of the celebrated Charles Darwin, On the Origin of Species *(London, 1859), broke with these incorrect views and called forth a complete revolution in the scientific thinking of its time. It is true that even before Darwin some outstanding scientists (G. L. Buffon, J. B. Lamarck, E. G. Saint-Hillaire, K. F. Rulje) had, far in advance of their time, protested against the creation myths of the ancient world, but the proofs for the theory of evolution which they put were not sufficiently well-founded, and thus carried little weight. Darwin was the first to prove clearly and convincingly that all living beings, plants as well as animals, and even man himself, are the products of a long historical evolutionary process and not the result of some mysterious supernatural creation or of mere chance. Darwin supported his theory by many proofs not only from the different biological sciences, chiefly from taxonomy, comparative anatomy, embryology and paleontology but also from the experience and results obtained by agriculturists, both breeders and cultivators. The theory which Darwin formulated is still valid in its essential features, although, naturally, his successors have enlarged it, deepened it and, where necessary, corrected its shortcomings. Today there is probably no scientist whose work does not start from the foundations laid by Darwin's theory and from Darwin's historical conception of the question of the origin of the species.*

We know a number of factors which enable us to understand the laws which govern the evolution of all living things, and the paths which that evolution follows. Thus we know today that evolution proceeded always from what was very simple to what is very complex, from primitive to specialised forms. We know today that plants and animals always are ecologically dependent on their environment. Any changes in this environment called forth and also conditioned changes in the organisms. The unceasing and gradual changes in the environment forced the organisms to pass through a series of small, imperceptible changes, which made it possible for them to continue living in the new, changing environment, and which at the same time enriched the biosphere by new types. Besides these relatively long periods of gradual and continuous evolution and adaptation (evolution in the narrower sense of the word), there were also the revolutionary changes or leaps in the development of the Earth's surface, (i.e. orogenic processes), or of its climate (i.e. the Ice Ages), followed by qualitative changes and evolutionary leaps in the historical development of life (evolutionary revolutions). In this way the higher levels of organisation of living matter arose, and the organisms themselves acquired new characters necessary for life in the new environment. It goes without saying that the interconnection and interdependence of individuals of the same species, as well as the concurrence in time and space of different species, are intimately related to the ecological equilibrium of the organisms and their environment, and that there exists also a close interaction between the form and the function of the various organs of the body.

Paleontology has done much for the victory of the theory of evolution and will still do much. This is its duty, for comparative anatomy has shown that evolution is possible, comparative embryology that it is probable, and paleontology that it is true!

The theory of evolution shows clearly that all living things developed gradually from the simplest to the most complex, from protozoans to man, and that life really resembles a strong and richly-branched tree. This gigantic tree of life, on which some branches dried up long ago while others are only now withering, and still others luxuriantly burgeon forth, could grow and really has grown solely and exclusively from the laborious work and scientific curiosity and perseverance of paleontologists, zoologists, botanists, comparative anatomists, embryologists, and to some extent, physiologists. This gigantic tree of life shows us the ancestors, brothers, cousins, and even the most distant relatives of each member of it.

As, however, the crown of this gigantic tree of life is extremely thick, so that the individual branches and twigs are often lost in the shadows of others, we have not as yet established a sufficient number of facts for us to know it in its whole surprising richness. Therefore we overcome the gaps in our present knowledge by more or less ingenious assumptions, theories and hypotheses, in order to explain what for the present we do not know, what for the present is lacking in our proofs, but what is necessary for explaining a problem and formulating a conclusion.

But working theories or hypotheses are not facts. They are mere assumptions put forward by the student of a problem, not only on the basis of his knowledge and experience, but also prompted by his intuition; they are only assumptions starting from many facts and explaining others which have not yet been elucidated, and for the present perhaps even cannot be elucidated in any other way. Every working theory or hypothesis is only an aid to further work, and newly-ascertained facts may confirm it, correct it, supplement it, or refute it. Thus it is the duty of every scientist always to draw attention to what in his work or in his conclusions is built on direct proof and what on conjecture, what in his work and conclusions is certain and what assumed. We too shall do so in our present study, and all the more so in order that those readers desirous of knowledge, to whom this book is dedicated in the first instance, may readily distinguish between what science already knows and what it only provisionally assumes.

But let us start on our journey into the depths of primeval time, and let us observe the many-coloured mosaic of life from its simple and humble beginning to its manifold complexity of today.

All living nature around us, all plants and animals, in short all living beings, man not excepted, are the result of an unimaginably long process of evolution, which started together with the origin of living matter and which has constantly characterised it since that time at least 1,500 million years ago. The present stage in the evolution of organisms is of course neither constant nor permanent: it is only the latest but not the last stage, it is only the present time of what will itself be the past in the future.

All organisms living today, from protozoans to man, are linked to each other by direct or indirect ties of relationship, reaching deep into the past of our Earth, and indicating their common origin from the initial flakes or droplets of living matter, from the initial scraps of protein.

AT THE SOURCE OF LIFE

The earliest trace of life on our Earth consisted of a kind of protein scrap and was without any membranes, undifferentiated into nucleus and cytoplasm; it was so simple that compared with it even the simplest organisms of today seem very complex and perfect. The first trace of life appeared at the end of the Archeozoic, in the primeval oceanic period, when a fall in temperature made the water vapours in the atmosphere condense and form the earliest primeval oceans in the depressions of the solidified crust of the Earth.

No traces of this primordial life have been preserved, as the ancient rocks in which we must look for the cradle of life were for endless ages constantly exposed to the most varied upheavals of the Earth's crust, and as these earliest bits of protein had neither any firm shells nor any supporting skeletons, all traces of them have vanished. However, A. I. Oparin among others has recently succeeded in explaining the most probable way in which they developed from inorganic matter. It is from these bits of protein that the simplest, primeval organisms developed. It is certain that these fundamental organisms were not yet distinctly differentiated into the two basic kingdoms of living beings, into plants and animals. This differentiation occurred, however, relatively early, and it is the first and fundamental step in biological and evolutionary progress. According to A. I. Oparin, this change was a direct outcome of that in the state of their environment, by which these organisms could draw less and less upon simple organic substances in their environment for the maintenance of their existence and were forced more and more to produce for themselves organic substances from inorganic ones. Some of them did not succeed in doing so and perished, while others succeeded and laid the first foundations for the development of the vegetable kingdom, whose members are still today not tied by their existence to other organic matter, insofar of course as they are not parasites, but are able to live autotrophically i.e. they can—like for instance the green plants of today—assimilate inorganic substances from their environment (carbon dioxide from the air, and water, and mineral salts dissolved in it, from the soil), and with the help of the energy of the Sun transform these simple substances into very complex organic compounds (proteins, fats, sugar, starch, etc.) from which they then build up their bodies. This capacity for independent nutrition is also today a characteristic feature of plants, and one by which they distinguish themselves considerably from animals, whose nutrition is heterotrophic, i.e. dependent on substances formed by other organisms. From this point of view the *origin of life* is really only the *origin of plants*, including viruses and bacteria, for we have to regard the animal kingdom as a lateral branch which subsequently grew out from the stock of the plants. Almost all contemporary paleontologists and biologists subscribe today to this conception of the precedence of organisms living on inorganic substances taken from their environment, i.e. to the theory of the primary origin of the vegetable form of existence of living matter.

Thus we see in the evolution of life two large main lines which formed two vast kingdoms, *the vegetable kingdom* numbering today more than 300,000 species, and the *animal kingdom* numbering today more than 1,000,000 species (chiefly insects). This vast and surprising multiplicity of plant and animal forms is mainly the result of the capacity of living matter to adapt itself to the most varied conditions of its outer environment on our Earth, i.e. the plant and animal forms were able to adapt themselves to life in salt waters and here again in deep waters as well as in shallow ones, in fresh waters and in brackish waters; they were able to adapt themselves to life in the polar zone and in the tropical zone, in hot and dry deserts and in cold tundras, high in the mountains and deep under ground, and they were able also to change with the changing conditions of the different outer environments.

The oldest organisms on our Earth were thus plants which were able to nourish themselves, which did not need somebody to prepare their food for them; inorganic substances were sufficient for them, and they were able by different processes to build from them all the complex organic components of their bodies.

It is certainly an interesting question which vegetable type should be regarded as phylogenetically oldest. Many scientists assume that the *primary form of the plant existence of living matter* probably resembled most closely the autotrophic *bacteria* of today. Others again imagine the oldest vegetable type in the form of *blue-green algae* (Cyanophyceae). The bacteria as well as the blue-green algae belong to the organisms whose cell has not yet any separate nucleus.

Can paleontology prove that bacteria and blue-green algae lived even in the oldest time of our Earth? It can! In the pageant of creation, bacteria as well as blue algae are represented. The difficulty is, however, that one cannot say with certainty that for instance the bacteria are the oldest beings we know; for the oldest bacteria have been discovered only in the Algonkian, that is at a time when numerous higher organisms already existed—such as radiolaria, worms, crustaceans, and echinoderms, whose remains have been well, even though rarely, preserved. This fact must not, however, mislead us, for we have to remember that the geological age in which they are first discovered need not also be the age of their origin. We do not know them from the Archeozoic for the simple reason that we do not know the Archeozoic world at all.

But we are not interested only in the picture of the first organism; what really concerns us here is its importance for the origin of a higher organic type, and in this connection the evidence is unequivocal. During the whole of their truly inconceivably long existence on the Earth the bacteria as well as the blue-green algae have gone their separate ways, preserving until today many of the features and characters which they acquired at the very beginning of their life. They always followed their own way without becoming the starting point for new and more highly organised types.

But besides the bacteria and blue algae there lived at that time another group of primary organisms, the *Flagellata*. This group is still in existence today and includes various microscopic organisms on the border between the vegetable and animal kingdoms. It was certain types of these Flagellata which became the starting point for the two main evolutionary paths taken by both the organic kingdoms with the path of the vegetable kingdom going a little further back, as the older.

Today we know for certain that various types of algae, especially various lower types of green algae, developed from the Flagellata, while there are many reasons for accepting the view that the Fungi did also develop from the Flagellata.

It is also among the Flagellata that we have to search for the origin of the first animals, the Protozoa, for there exist many affinities and evolutionary relations between certain groups of the Flagellata on the one hand and the heterotrophic, primitive Protozoa on the other.

Thus the Flagellata not only give us a picture of one of the primary organisms, but also are types from which one can derive the evolution of the two branches of organic life, plants and animals. The features and properties which characterise them prove that in ancient times they had the ability to become the foundation stone for the development of originally primitive life to a higher level, and thus to permit the growth of the vegetable branch and later also of the animal branch. These features and properties can still be observed today, and make both zoologists and botanists regard the Flagellata as belonging to their field. It is very rare to find fossil Flagellata in the old geological formations, and it is not until the Cretaceous formation at the end of the Mesozoic that such finds become at all frequent.

As soon as some Flagellata, thanks to their potentialities, had proved capable of laying the foundations for the origin of new, higher types, there occurred the first evolutionary flowering of nature, which began to develop in all directions. But so far we know very little about this first flowering nor do we know much about the forms and paths of this primary development, as the first distinct remains of an organic nature only come from the Proterozoic, that is from a time when life had already become far more developed and differentiated. From the Proterozoic we have, however, indubitable remains of algae, coelenterates, worms, brachiopods, crinoids, crustaceans and other types, of which some already belong to highly organised groups. Although finds from the Proterozoic are rare, those fossils which are found show clearly that in the Proterozoic the evolution of plants and animals had been going on for an immensely long time, and that what we know today is only a section of the last phase of this primeval evolution.

The evidence that we possess indicates that even then life took many different forms in the Proterozoic seas, and that it was confined exclusively to water. The continents were still desert, without life; and a long time had to elapse before life left the water and passed on to dry land. Thus *the sea was the cradle of life*, and the first evolution of creation took place in the seas.

JOURNEY INTO THE DEPTHS OF PRIMEVAL TIME

The geologist and the paleontologist, like the historian, divide the past into several basic periods; for them such divisions of time are especially necessary, since without these they would all too easily lose their bearings in the immensely long history of the Earth and its creatures. The story of the Earth and of life has its own prehistory, its Antiquity, its Middle Ages, and its Modern Times, but each of these periods lasted many millions of years instead of mere centuries. The milestones of the main geological eras or epochs are the orogenetic (mountain-forming) periods; each of them changed the distribution of land and sea, and altered the environment of creation, which then either adapted itself or became extinct. Thus new and more advanced branches of life originated, while those incapable of evolution and transformation died out.

The prehistory of our Earth begins with its origin, which is explained by cosmogonic theories. The initial period is the epoch in which the surface of our Earth was still a molten mass, offering no opportunities for the origin of life. This age is removed from us by at least two thousand five hundred million years, but there are many estimates that this time-span is much longer, even as much as four to five thousand million years.

The geological history proper of the Earth begins only with the time when the solid crust of the Earth was formed. This happened in the so-called *Archeozoic Era* or *Age*. The Archeozoic Era is divided into an earlier, waterless (anhydric) period and a later, primeval-ocean period when the lowering of the temperature made the water vapours condense and form the first primeval oceans in the depressions of the solidifying crust. Volcanic activity was great at the time. Hot vapours, gases, boiling waters and immense lava flows pressed upward through the hardly-congealed crust of the Earth. The lavas solidified both on the surface and below it, and were transformed into rocks. Before they set, they yielded up the most valuable material they held, precipitating metals and their ores. Gases still continued to escape from them for a long time, carrying to the surface what had been born in the greatest depths. Many such lava flows were piled up one above the other, causing the first unevennesses on the Earth's surface and the first erosive activity of the primeval rivers, which then transported masses of material into the primeval oceans, there to form the first sediments at the bottom. We find today only insignificant traces of these oldest lava flows. Rivers, glaciers, wind, sea, new volcanic activity succeeded each other in the same place in the long geological epoch that followed and all this effaced the primary volcanic appearance of the Earth and formed its chequered geological past.

The first relief on the Earth's crust, not unlike the present surface of the Moon, was thus caused by volcanic activity. Today no traces of it have remained. The rocks weathered and crumbled, and the waters carried away the pulverised residue and, after grinding it, turned it into sand and mud at the sea bottom. After a very long time, when the diagenetic processes had consolidated the sand and mud into sandy and marly rocks, these might be uplifted by orogenetic forces above the sea level. The original sea bottom became dry land again. Wind, water and other geological agents ferociously bit into the exposed and undisturbed rocks, and gnawed them until they disintegrated, and the process of erosion, transport, sedimentation, uplifting, began all over again. But it might also happen that the Earth's crust opened afresh, and new streams of molten lava poured forth from the gaping fissures and crevices, remelted the older rocks, and formed new ones, often harder than the original. This certainly happened many times before any part of an ancient continent was formed that has survived until today, which we must regard with the respect due to one of the oldest monuments of the geological history of our Earth.

GEOLOGICAL TIME-TABLE

Era	Period		Duration in millions of years	Distance from us in time in millions of years
QUATERNARY (Anthropozoic) *Age of Man*		Holocene (present age)	1	
		Pleistocene		
TERTIARY (Cenozoic) *Age of Mammals*	Neogene	Pliocene	10	
		Miocene	15	
	Paleogene	Oligocene	15	
		Eocene	20	
		Paleocene	10	70
MESOZOIC *Age of Reptiles*		Cretaceous	70	140
		Jurassic	45	185
		Triassic	40	225
PALEOZOIC *Age of Invertebrates, Fishes and Amphibia*	Upper	Permian	45	270
		Carboniferous	50	320
	Lower	Devonian	80	400
		Silurian	20	420
		Ordovician	60	480
		Cambrian	90-120	570-600
PROTEROZOIC (Eozoic) *Development of the Invertebrates*		Algonkian	about 1000-1500	
		Huronian		
ARCHAEAN (Archeozoic)		Primeval Oceanic period *(with the Origin of Life)*	2000-3000	*(1500-2000)*
		Anhydric (waterless) period		
Period of origin of the Earth's crust			at least 4000-6000	

On the whole it must be said that we still know very little of the earliest geological history of the Earth. This is not surprising, considering that this primeval history began at least 2500 million years ago. However, we know much more of the later history. We know when and where there were formerly continents and seas, when and where there were vast and empty deserts or ice fields, where there were luxuriant virgin forests, where vast volcanic areas, where wide open regions with lakes and swamps. We know when and where sea bottoms became dry land, and dry land sea bottoms. We know in which ages and where soaring mountains were lifted up by huge orogenetic forces, and we know how long it took before they were again lowered into peneplains by erosion and denudation. We know what the climate was like in the different geological ages and when it changed. We know what plants and animals lived in the different geological ages and how they lived, and we know many other things beside. In fact our knowledge has accumulated to such an extent, showing us so clearly the time sequence of development, that we are able now to establish further epochs after the Archeozoic Era, and we distinguish now the following five eras: *the Proterozoic, the Paleozoic, the Mesozoic, the Cenozoic* (Tertiary) and *the Anthropozoic* (Quaternary) eras. Each of these geological eras is so long that we subdivide them into geological formations, of which there were for instance six in the Paleozoic: Cambrian, Ordovician, Silurian, Devonian, Carboniferous and Permian. When necessary, the geological formations are divided into still smaller time sections; thus the Permian is divided into the younger Zechstein and the older Rotliegendes. (See the table of geological times).

The historical past of the Earth corresponds to the *historical development of the animals*. While the development of life fell at the end of the Archeozoic age, the Proterozoic is the age of the development of the invertebrates; the Paleozoic is the age of the flourishing of invertebrates, fish and amphibia, the Mesozoic is the age of reptiles, the Tertiary the age of mammals and the Quaternary the age of man. The *development of the plants* occurred a little earlier than the development of the animals, as the Antiquity of plants, the Paleophytic, characterised by the flourishing of cryptogams, ends with the Lower Permian; their Middle Ages, the Mesophytic, characterised by the flourishing of gymnosperms, begins with the Upper Permian and ends with the Lower Cretaceous and their Modern Times, the Cenophytic or Neophytic, characterised by the flourishing of angiosperms, begins with the Upper Cretaceous and still continues today.

The history of the Earth and of life on it embraces an inconceivably long time. We have already said that at least two thousand five hundred million years have passed since the initial molten stage of our Earth. We can make this vast span of time more comprehensible by reducing it to some current unit, such as a year. In this way the geological past of the Earth will be distributed over the year in something like the following way: the Archeozoic and Proterozoic epochs correspond almost to the first three quarters of the year, so that these two epochs taken together last approximately from the beginning of January to the second half of September. The formation of the primeval crust of the Earth falls in early Spring, but as yet there are no primeval oceans, and life has not appeared. The origin of life occurs about the beginning of May; the first development of the invertebrates in the Proterozoic lasts all through the summer and the beginning of autumn till about the middle of September. Then the Paleozoic begins with the flourishing of the invertebrates, fish and amphibia, and lasts till the last days of November, only to give place to the Mesozoic, the age of the giant reptiles, which lasts till the beginning of the last week of December. The last week of the year is then divided between the Tertiary, marked by the flourishing of the mammals, and the Quaternary, memorable for the origin of man. However, of this last week more than six days fall to the Tertiary, and only a part of one day to the Quaternary, the age of man, and it is not till about 8 p.m. of that day that the real ascent of man from his animal ancestors begins, and after several evolutionary stages have been gone through that the type of present man evolves. The history of human culture and science represents on this scale only a very small span of time corresponding to the last few minutes of the whole year of evolution. The above transposition of the millions of years of evolution into the terms of one year shows clearly that the older a geological epoch is, the longer it is, and that the evolutionary history of man, and still more his cultural history, is, when compared with the history of the Earth and the history of other living beings, only a brief episodic chapter in the great chronicle of nature.

Knowing now the stages of the road which we intend to follow from the origin of life to the age of man, let us walk down that road, noting all the multiplicity of life which it has to show us.

THE PRIMEVAL EVOLUTION OF THE PLANTS

Over the boundless plain of the primeval ocean, far away on the eastern horizon, the golden disk of the sun rises from the rosy cradle of the dawn, casting light and warmth in all directions. Wavelets driven by a gentle breeze sparkle in the light as they hurry shorewards.

For endless distances yellow sands and jagged rocks lined the shores of the first ocean and extended far inland. But sand and rocks were alike desert, barren of the smallest and simplest form of life, for in these ancient times towards the end of the Archeozoic age life had not as yet conquered the dry land. Neither in the Proterozoic nor at the beginning of the Paleozoic had it succeeded in doing so. And thus there brooded over this empty wilderness a deep, heavy silence interrupted only by the thunder of tempestuous storms, by the shrieking of gales, or by a boulder detaching itself from some rock and cannonading down the steep mountain side or falling with a mighty splash into the ocean.

The continents of the whole world of that time were lifeless desert. But in the waters of the first ocean life developed and gradually increased on every side.

THE DAWN OF PLANT LIFE

As we saw above, it was the Flagellata which came to play the important role in evolution, even though we also know of other types of organisms which may show us what the first living creatures looked like according to our theories.

The first *algae* certainly developed from the unicellular Flagellata. These algae were among the first habitants of our Earth, and their first evolutionary types were also to begin with the unicellular. The polycellular algae are younger than these earlier ones and already represent a higher form of evolution.

From the evolutionary viewpoint the algae represent a great step forward. They show quite clearly the most important adaptation, which was directed first of all towards improved intake of food and subsequently to a suitable means of reproduction in order to safeguard the existence of the genus.

It is natural that the adaptation directed towards a more perfect intake of food should show itself first of all by an increase in the surface of the body, as this increased the surface of contact with the nourishment in the environment. We can already observe this increase in the unicellular algae, whose mainly globular bodies carry many apophyses of the most diverse shapes. The algae of the group Siphonales attain considerable dimensions, sometimes even as much as two feet; the disappearance of the septa makes them give the impression of being unicellular, though in reality they may not be so. Their polynuclear body (thallus) acquires by branching not only a considerable size but also a complex shape; thus for instance in the marine algae of the genus *Caulerpa* the thallus is so strangely divided that some of its formations are reminiscent of leaves, others of stalk and roots. However, this path of evolution, defined by the heightening of the complexity of a unicellular (or apparently unicellular) organism, ended in a blind alley and did not lead to any further development in the organic world. As P. A. Baranov puts it, 'The most important upward path in the differentiation of the body of the organism was the path of the origin and further development of polycellular organisms. These existed in the beginning in the form of simple filaments, then there appeared filaments of the most diverse shapes, and finally intricately-built large bodies (thalli) differentiated into various organs and attached to the sea bed.' This path of enlarging the surface of contact of the body with the environment for the purpose of increasing nutrition proved evolutionarily more correct and more valuable, and together with many other improvements led in the course of further evolution to the origin of a higher type of plant.

In addition to improved intake of food the origin of the sex process is also important in the evolution of the algae and constitutes a great progress in evolution.

Before the algae arose all the more primitive organisms (i.e. bacteria, blue algae and Flagellata) multiplied only asexually (vegetatively). In asexual procreation, however, the reproducing organisms continue their development as it were directly in their descendants; the sex process on the other hand leads always to a new evolutionary line. But in order that a sex process may be established male and female gametes have to be formed in the organisms. The gametes are special cells—biologically, but not chemically, the most complex ones of all, and it is these that carry the hereditary characters. The gametes fuse, form a new cell, the so-called zygote, from which an organism with a double heredity—paternal and maternal—develops.

Though we find asexual propagation in the algae, yet we can also discover in them from the first time sexual propagation. In its simplest form this consists of the fusion of two equal cells among the unicellular algae; this type has been preserved to this day by some Volvocaceae closely akin to the Flagellata. A simple form of the sex process may also be seen in the filamentary algae, for instance in the recent algae of the genus *Spirogyra*. The process is effected by two filaments of the algae approaching each other so that two cells, one from each filament (or sometimes all the cells of the two filaments) enter a so-called copulation channel formed by the arching of their membranes and their solution along the contact surface; the plasmatic contents of the two cells then fuse into one, the so-called zygote, through this channel, and a new individual arises from the zygote.

This simple sex process was perfected by the development of specialised sex cells, male and female. These were at first equal in size, but later the male one grew small, while the female one grew big, until finally the female cell lost its mobility, while the smaller male cell preserved it. In the further course of evolution the higher algae developed also special sex organs: a male organ, known as the antheridium, in which the male sex cells (spermatozoides) formed, and a female organ, the so-called oogonium, in which the ovum took shape.

It is certain that it took several hundreds of millions of years for the algae to develop from their primitive forms to their most perfect, i.e. to types with complex organisation having specialised tissues and a characteristic sex process. These higher algae offered all the conditions necessary for a further evolution of the vegetable kingdom, so that new, higher and still more perfect plant types might arise from them. We shall see later that this actually did happen.

We may say that the algae really are among the most ancient inhabitants of our Earth. Their first beginning and expansion occurred towards the end of the Archeozoic, as may be proved indirectly from the stratified accumulation of a coaly substance in the metamorphosed sediments of Finland and Russia which date from the Archeozoic age. This coaly substance is an anthracite rich in ashes, which, owing to the metamorphism, shows the mineralogical properties of graphite. This graphitic coal seam is called shungite and attains a thickness of up to six feet, and was formed by the accumulation of some primitive algae. Although we know a few algae from the Proterozoic, it is not until the beginning of the Paleozoic, the Cambrian, Ordovician and Silurian, that we find them in large numbers. In addition to many species about whose evolutionary status we do not know much at present, a good many specimens of green and red algae have been preserved from the ancient times, and, even more commonly, examples of those genera whose thalli were encrusted with calcium carbonate, and which therefore were easily fossilised: such genera, for instance, as *Dasyporella*, *Sphaerocodium* and *Sollenopora*. It is only very rarely that genera whose thalli were not so encrusted have been preserved. The graptolite shales afford a further proof of the occurrence of vast numbers of algae in the Lower Paleozoic seas, in the Silurian. These shales received their name from the multitude of beautifully-preserved graptolites found in them. The shales themselves consist of clayey or limey rocks with perfect cleavage and coloured dark or black by a finely-disseminated carbonaceous substance. It is generally assumed that this substance was formed from the disintegrated and carbonised thalli of the marine algae which lived in the calms of the Silurian seas, and which there had as favourable an environment for expansion as their descendants of today have in our 'Sargasso Sea' with its luxuriant crop of seaweed of the genus *Sargassum.*

In the early days of paleontological research scientists distinguished many more species of ancient algae than today, the reason being that later research has shown that many finds described and designated as remains of Lower Paleozoic algae are really only traces of the creeping or burrowing activity of animals, or simply the results of purely mechanical events. Nevertheless the evidence is sufficiently large to prove that the algae had expanded fully and were already flourishing in those ancient times.

THE PLANTS CONQUER THE DRY LAND

The quiet expansion of the algae, which is the very first stage in the evolution of the plants, was suddenly interrupted towards the end of the Silurian by a great geological upheaval, when the orogenetical stresses of the so-called Caledonian folding caused new continents and new mountains to emerge from the bottom of the seas. All of a sudden many algae were forced to live in lakes and swamps which dried up or grew less and less salty. These new conditions of a changing environment also had a profound repercussion on the algae, and stimulated in some of them considerable bodily changes. Thus we stand here at the beginning of a new, very important turn or leap in the evolution of the plants, at the beginning of the stage in which the *transition of the plants from water to dry land* took place. This event occurred some four hundred million years ago.

The conditions for the life of plants on land not only differed from those of their life in water, but were also far more diverse and variable. In the water the plants had not been in danger of dehydration, whereas on land the struggle against this danger was the prime necessity of life; thus the plants were forced to form a special covering tissue, an epidermis. In the water the plant absorbed its food with the whole surface of its body, but on land it was necessary to develop special organs for the intake and distribution of water with mineral substances from the soil dissolved in it. In the water the plant did not need any special mechanism for the exchange of the two gases, oxygen and carbon dioxide; on land it had to form the so-called pores between the cells of the epidermis for this purpose. In the water the plant's body did not need any supporting tissues, but these were necessary for life on land. In short, everything which had been an advantage to plants when living in water, and which they had developed in the course of a long evolution, had to be radically changed in their transition to life on land.

The plants' conquest of land took place at the very end of the Silurian and at the beginning of the Devonian. The oldest representatives of the land plants are the most primitive type of vascular cryptogams, to which none of the present forms appear to be related; they are the *Psilophytales*. Their axes grew from bulbous or creeping rootstocks, ramified furcately, and carried spore vessels at their tops. They were leafless (e.g. the herb genera *Rhynia* and *Horneophyton* or the tree-like *Pseudosporochus*) or leafy (e.g. *Psilophyton, Drepanophycus, Asteroxylon*). Some of these types also grew in the mud of the shallow coastal waters, e.g. *Taeniocrada, Zosterophyllum.* Their outer simplicity of form must not mislead us as to their anatomical structure. In the course of the evolution from algae to Psilophytes life had taken a great leap forward. The whole body of the Psilophytes was already covered with a cuticle with pores through which carbon dioxide penetrated into the plant, and through which the surplus water and liberated oxygen left the plant; the plant had already developed tissues with definite functions, and for the first time lignin appears, a chemical substance rendering the cell walls woody. These and still other features—as for instance a further perfection of the sex process, which resembled that of the present ferns—indicate distinctly the great evolutionary progress of the Psilophytes as compared with the algae, and the far-reaching changes in the morphological structures and biochemical processes of the descendants as compared with their forebears. We do not yet know from which types of algae the Psilophytes arose; but it is commonly assumed that they developed most probably from the green algae, as green is a characteristic of the flora of dry land.

The origin and expansion of the Psilophytes form a very important stage in the evolution of the plants. In a geological sense the age of the Psilophytes was relatively short, as it lasted only between twenty and thirty million years. The first Psilophytes appeared towards the end of the Silurian; from the middle of the Devonian their numbers steadily decreased, until they completely disappeared at the end of that period. But before they became extinct some of the types belonging to them had developed into the first representatives of the lycopods (*Protolepidodendron, Barrandeina, Duisbergia*), horsetails (*Calamophyton, Hyenia*) and ferns (*Protopteridium*), which marked the Middle and Upper Devonian landscape.

IN THE PRIMEVAL CARBONIFEROUS FORESTS

The evolution of the primary flora of the land lasted all through the Middle and Upper Devonian. At the beginning of the Carboniferous, however, the great orogenetic processes of the Hercynian folding gave impetus to a great evolutionary activity within the plant kingdom. The massive high mountains produced by the Hercynian orogeny were rapidly lowered by the action of exogenous geological agents. Great floods and huge rivers washed vast amounts of waste, sand, and dust into the large basins at the foot of the mountains, and a luxuriant vegetation grew up in the exceptionally favourable living conditions offered by these basins, so rich in water. The climate was moist and hot, and the air was strongly impregnated with the carbon dioxide which had got into the atmosphere from the many active volcanoes. These favourable conditions furthered not only the evolution and expansion of the flora, but also its luxuriant, often tree-like growth. For the first time in the history of the Earth primeval forests began to grow.

The most characteristic members of the *primeval carboniferous forests* were the gigantic lycopods, forty-five to ninety feet high, whose crowns were either richly branched (*Lepidodendron, Lepidophlois, Bothrodendron*) or ended in tufts of long and narrow leaves (*Sigillaria*), while their trunks were studded with ornamental scars left by the leaves that had been shed. Large sporangial cones grew from the trunks or branches, or hung at the end of the twigs on the tree-tops. The arboreal horse-tails, calamites (*Eucalamites, Stylocalamites, Calamitina*) rivalled the tree-like lycopods in height; their large, articulated trunks, distinguished by longitudinal ribs, grew directly from the shallow coastal waters of lakes and swamps. Narrow, linear leaves (*Annularia, Asterophyllites*) grew from the branches in whorls, as did the branches from the trunk. Below these tree-giants, lycopods and horse-tails, spread a low luxuriant undergrowth of mosses, hepaticae, herbaceous and creeping lycopods and magnificent clumps of the most diverse low ferns. But here there were also such ferns as *Mariopteris, Etapteris* and many others of their kind which wound themselves like lianas round the trunks of lepidodendrons, sigillariae and others, and pushed upwards towards the light, or which like beautiful trees gathered their big leaf-fans into ostentatious crowns, thirty to forty-five feet above the ground.

Vascular cryptogams were not the only tree-like plants which had their home in the Carboniferous forests, for remarkable representatives of the extinct group Pteridospermae also grew up in these forests. The Pteridospermae occupy the lowest place among the *gymnosperms* in the paleobotanical system; they were the first gymnosperms to appear on Earth, and their earliest representatives are found even among the Upper Devonian flora. They resemble the ferns very closely in appearance, but unlike the ferns they do not form sporangia and spores but real seeds. The Pteridospermae (*Neuropteris, Odontopteris,* certain types of the genus *Sphenopteris* and many others) are extremely important from an evolutionary point of view, as they show the path by which the first gymnosperms developed from the cryptogams. There was an abundance of Pteridospermae in the Carboniferous forests, and though they were of relatively low growth, they had unusually large leaf-fans. On the other hand the *Cordaites*, another group of gymnosperms of the Carboniferous forests, formed tall trees up to one hundred and thirty feet high, with a smooth trunk reminiscent of our beeches, and with a richly branched crown with long, ribbon-like leaves. At the end of the Paleozoic, in the Permian, the Cordaites died out without leaving any descendants. The coniferous Walchia (*Lebachia Ernestiodendron*) were in terms of evolution the highest plant type in the Carboniferous forests. They too were trees, often large ones, but it is only rarely that we find their remains in the Carboniferous sediments. This might lead us to infer that Walchia were still rare in the Carboniferous, were it not for the fact that we know that they belonged to the most abundant and most common plant types even at the beginning of the Permian. It is therefore more likely that even in the Carboniferous, the Walchia preferred drier, unwatered regions.

The Carboniferous Lycopodiaceae, Equisetaceae and ferns (Filices) had many important advantages over the Psilophytes, from which they originated. First and foremost they had a well-developed root system and good foliage, two features which together increased many times the effect of the food taken in by them. This, in conjunction with a more perfectly organised system of conductive tissues, made it possible for them to develop huge bodies and to spread rapidly. They completely gained the ascendancy over the Psilophytes, and during the whole of the Carboniferous and the Lower Permian they formed the predominating types of plant life on our Earth. Their rule lasted much longer than the rule of the Psilophytes, but it came to an end in the Upper Permian.

Although it is some 250 million years since the Carboniferous and the Lower Permian swamp forests grew on our Earth, yet they are of unusually great importance for our life today, for it is to them that we owe our *deposits of black coal*.These primeval forests were swamp forests, and when old age, tempests, or floods felled a tree, it lay on the bottom of the swamp, where broken-off branches, leaves and microscopic particles of vegetable matter also accumulated. From time to time layers of clay and sand covered these masses, which later underwent special chemical and fossilisation processes, and were also compressed by the weight of the overlying rocks, until finally the original vegetable matter was turned into black coal, the life-blood of all our present undertakings, the mainspring of all our industry. Where today derricks point to the sky, the roar of machinery is heard, and a rich and active life pulsates, there once, in the far past, huge swamp-forests held sway, drinking in the light of the sun, groaning under the water of cloudbursts, or shrouded in white veils of mist. There is a saying that 'coal is petrified darkness', but that is far from the truth. It was not darkness which gave us coal but brilliant sunshine, blue waters, and the bright green of plants.

Another great period in the evolution of the plants came to an end with the passing of the Carboniferous primeval forests. It had followed on the age of the algae, and it lasted from the appearance of the first Psilophytes, that is to say it extended from the end of the Silurian and the beginning of the Devonian till the end of the Lower Permian. It had been the age of the vascular cryptogams, which had marked the character of the flora, among which all other types, whether they were older and more primitive ones dying out or younger ones in a higher stage of evolution preparing to take over from the cryptogams, played only a subordinate role.

THE COLD WIND FROM THE ICE

Just as the orogenetic processes of the Caledonian and Hercynian foldings had a decisive influence on the origin of new environments, so did the radical changes in climate which occurred at the onset of the Ice Ages. In both cases the new environments confronted life with new conditions to which it had to react if it were not to perish. An Ice Age of this type also overtook the Carboniferous flora of the southern hemisphere. Even though we do not regard the southern flora as completely glacial, we have to assume that it met other living conditions than the contemporary northern flora. For this reason the growth of the southern flora was much lower and the flora itself more monotonous. The characteristic plants of the southern flora were species of the general *Glassopteris* and *Gangamopteris*, with large tongue-shaped leaves and with a rather puzzling position in the plant system. Besides these the equisetacean types *Schizoneura* and *Phyllotheca* were also representative of this flora.

From what has been said above, it clearly follows that even in the Carboniferous we can distinguish between *two large phytogeographical regions*, which differed considerably from each other in their flora. The first region includes Europe, North America, the northern part of Asia and North Africa, and is characterised by the so-called *European flora.* The second region includes the East Indies, South and Southeast Africa, South America and Australia, and is characterised by the so-called *Gondwana flora.* Although the two regions are fairly sharply separated from each other, there are areas in which the two floras overlap and intermingle, as for instance the northern part of European Russia and Siberia.

THE GYMNOSPERMS CONQUER THE WORLD

The age of the algae, the age of the psilophytes and the age of the vascular cryptogams, that is to say the epoch of plant evolution from the earliest times till the end of the Lower Permian, are known as the *Antiquity of the flora*, the Paleophytic, distinguished by the rich expansion and flourishing of the cryptogams, which characterised the Earth in those ages. However, in the Upper Permian a striking change took place. The flora of the coal-forming swamps of the Carboniferous and Lower Permian had almost completely disappeared; instead there appeared an abundance of gymnosperms (*Ullmania, Baiera, Voltzia*), which proved to be the precursors of the great expansion of the gymnosperms typical of almost the whole of the Mesozoic.

This expansion marks another great step in the progress of evolution. The appearance of the first seed-plants in the Upper Devonian and Carboniferous was a remarkable event. Exactly how remarkable it was cannot be understood, however, until we know something more about the propagation of plants. When a spore from the sporangium of a Pteridophyte falls on moist soil there develops from it a so-called gametophyte with sex organs. If the plant develops different kinds of spores, then a gametophyte with female organs develops from the large spore and one with male organs from the small spore. For fertilisation it is necessary for the male sex cell to get into the archegonium, and for this an aquatic environment is necessary. Without the presence of water fertilisation cannot take place. This dependence of all recent and extinct Pteridophytes (and also of course of the earlier developed psilophytes) on an aquatic, or at least a very moist environment, not only indicates that they originated from aquatic plants, but also shows how restricted their distribution must always be, as they are bound in this way exclusively to moist habitats. The very first seed-plants emancipated themselves from this dependence; their fertilisation took place without water (the pollen was for instance transported by the wind), and the seed developed on the plant itself, not outside it. But this was not the only advantage. While the spore is only one cell with a restricted amount of stored nutritive substances, the seed is multicellular and has a great amount of stored nutritive substances for the development of the germ. In addition the seed-case has become a good protection for the germ against unfavourable outside influences. All this was of outstanding evolutionary importance, as it afforded better conditions for the survival and continuation of the species. The first seed-plants had seed-vessels which developed on particularly specialised leaves; they lay uncovered on these leaves, and the seeds developing from the seed-vessels were 'naked'; hence plants with uncovered seed-vessels and seeds are called gymnosperms.

From an evolutionary point of view the appearance of seeds in plants is first and foremost an expression of the adaptation of the plants to drier regions in order to safeguard their progeny. But this was not the only change which the plants had to undergo in their conquest of the drier regions of the continents; changes also took place in their tissues, and the means of distributing substances in the body was perfected.

While the adaptation of some plant types to drier regions in the Devonian and Carboniferous had been of a rather local character, it became of general significance towards the end of the Carboniferous in consequence of a change of climate. Towards the end of the Carboniferous the moist climate changed to a drier one, the extensive swamps and bogs steadily decreased, and sandy and stony deserts came more and more to take their place over larger and larger areas. Even in the Lower Permian primitive types of vascular cryptogams grew here and there around the remaining swamps, as the only green oases in the sea of sand, and when towards the end of the Lower Permian the original moist climate had changed to an arid one even these primitive vascular cryptogams disappeared for ever. It was really only the higher gymnosperms which survived this great change of climate; the Carboniferous Pteridospermae, the lowest of the gymnosperms, were unable to withstand the changed conditions and the tree-like Lycopodia and Equiseta vanished with them. Only the higher, more specialised types of gymnosperms were able to adapt themselves to the new environment. Their victory marked a new epoch in the evolution of the plants. This is called the *Middle Ages of the plants*, the Mesophytic; it is characterised by the unusual expansion and flourishing of the gymnosperms and lasts almost till the very end of the Mesozoic, i.e. till the beginning of the Upper Cretaceous.

The most important among the gymnosperms were remarkably varied representatives of the cycadophytes, whether low with short, globular or barrel-shaped trunks (*Cycadoidea*), or of tree-like shape with slender, only rarely dividing stems, but both with a rich crown of long and tough leaves, mostly of a palm-like appearance. Among these cycadophytes it is the representatives of the now extinct group of Bennettitaceae of shrub-like (e.g. *Wielandiella, Williamsoniella*) or tree-like shape (e.g. *Williamsonia*) which are of particular importance for the study of the evolution of plants, for it is they which enable us to understand the relation between the gymnosperms and the vascular cryptogams on the one hand and between the gymnosperms and the angiosperms on the other. Besides cycadophytes there occurred rather abundantly such representatives of conifers as Ginkgoales (also the genus *Ginkgo* itself), taxodiums and trees of a pine-like and cypress-like nature. In this stage of the evolution of the flora the cryptogams completely lost their former leading position among the vegetation. It was only in shady and moist places or on the banks of some stream or lake that there grew various ferns (*Thaumatopteris, Dipteridium, Hausmannia* and others), though sometimes creeping ferns might also grow on rocks (as *Gleichenia*); various horse-tails grew from the waters of the pools (*Equisetites, Schizoneura*), but they did not attain such a great size as their predecessors, and their distribution was also much less wide.

THE VICTORY OF THE ANGIOSPERMS

The last epoch in the evolution of the flora dates from the beginning of the Upper Cretaceous; it is the so-called *Modern Times of the flora* (Cenophytic or Neophytic). As the two groups of angiosperms, the Monocotyledonae and the Dicotyledonae, appear side by side in the Upper Cretaceous, we cannot decide which of the two groups is the older.

Paleontological history tells us that the great change in the plants covering the Earth was not the result of a gradual replacement of gymnosperms by angiosperm flora, but was due to a quite sudden change-over. The suddenness of this replacement must of course be taken in the geological sense of the word 'sudden', that is, we must understand it to imply at least several hundreds of thousands of years. This transition from the rule of the gymnosperms to that of the angiosperms leads necessarily to the assumption that some corresponding changes occurred in the living conditions of the plants, and that these changes affected the whole Earth. We do not quite know what these were; perhaps they too were connected with orogenetic processes at the end of the Mesozoic and the beginning of the Tertiary and with changes of the climate and the distribution of land and sea. It is, however, certain that the large majority of the gymnospermic types were unable to adapt themselves to the changes in their outer environment and began to die out, while the evolutionally young and plastic type of angiospermic plants altered to meet the new living conditions, and thus quickly spread until finally it dominated the plant-life of the Earth.

The angiosperms are an evolutionally higher type than the gymnosperms, from which they originated.

They are, however, distinguished from these not only by having their seeds enclosed in a fruit, but also by most of them having their pistils and stamens covered by brightly-coloured petals and green sepals. In the history of the evolution of the plants the origin of the angiosperms from the gymnosperms represents a great forward leap, which made the angiosperms so remote from their gymnosperm ancestors that even today we cannot yet determine accurately which ancestors they had. There exist many theories and hypotheses as to the ancestors of the angiosperm (flowering) plants, but not one of these theories has been generally accepted. The solution of the problem is made exceptionally difficult by the fact that we most probably do not as yet know their oldest representatives. Their sudden appearance in innumerable families and genera in the Upper Cretaceous militates against the assumption that they originated then; on the contrary, it shows that they originated much earlier, that they arose in a tropical zone on one of the continents which later subsided under the waters of the ocean. If this is really so, then we cannot come to know their earliest representatives, as these will be deposited in the beds of the ocean floor. It is, however, certain that the descendants of these primary flowering plants also spread before the subsidence of the continent to rather distant regions, which still exist today as land, and that they there continued in their evolution. This theory at least explains satisfactorily the fact that the flowering plants appeared so suddenly and in so many forms as early as in the Upper Cretaceous.

According to the structure of the flower and wood, the magnolias, the tulip trees and other similar plants form the oldest types of the Cretaceous angiosperms. All of them are members of the order Ranunculales, with which as a rule the modern phylogenetic systems of the angiosperms begin. This seems to indicate that the ancestors of the angiosperms are to be found among the gymnosperms of the Cycadophytes or of the extinct Bennettitaceae.

The appearance of the angiosperms on Earth, and their early domination of the whole surface of the Earth, meant a great evolutionary advance. The dark and monotonous forests and clumps of gymnosperms were replaced by grassy meadows decked in the many-coloured mosaic of gay flowers, by shrubby thickets, and vast forests clad in different shades of green.Perennial and annual herbs appeared too, while many types of angiosperms adapted themselves also to an aquatic mode of life. This was a great feat of adaptation, for among gymnosperms there was not and is not a single herbal or aquatic type This expansion signified not only a victory for the vegetable kingdom but constituted also the indispensable precondition for the sudden explosive expansion of the animal kingdom, especially of the birds and mammals.

The types of angiosperm flora of the Upper Cretaceous and Lower Tertiary (Paleogene) prove that at that time there were as yet hardly any climatic differences between the various zones of the Earth's surface; as late as in the Eocene and Oligocene, palms and many other tropical and subtropical plants (fig-trees, cinnamomum, banana-trees, myrtles, acacias and others) grew in Central Europe. Even in the polar regions, in Greenland and on Spitzbergen, there was a warm and moist climate, and magnolias, laurels, chestnuts and other types of subtropical plants thrived in these regions.

But with the Neogene there came a change. Slowly but surely the palms and the other thermophile types retreated to the south, and in European latitudes a subtropical, but very moist climate prevailed, as is shown by the spread of deciduous forests composed of various oaks, nut-trees, elms, sumacs, plane-trees, chestnuts and other trees which today have their home in Southern Europe and in Transcaucasia. In the more northern regions coniferous forests predominated, composed mainly of firs and larches. In the Miocene, however, vast forests of various species of spruces, sequoias, larches and the now extinct glyptostrobes grew also in Central Europe.

The Tertiary flora too has proved of importance to industry and economic life, for the vast virgin forests, which grew up along the rivers and in their deltas as well as in the depressions at the foot of the mountains, have left Europe its deposits of *brown coal*, and although brown coal is less valuable than black coal as fuel, it is a most valuable raw material for industrial purposes. Many millions of years have passed since these brown coal forests first grew in the Tertiary, at least fifty million years separate the brown coal of today from the time when it first originated in the Paleogene swamp forests, and at least thirty million years from the time when it originated in the Neogene swamp forests.

VEGETATION AND THE ICE AGE

Throughout the whole of the Neogene the climate gradually grew more rigorous, with the result that towards the end of the Tertiary certain more warmth-loving members of the deciduous and coniferous forests retreated from Central Europe to the south, or even disappeared from Europe altogether.

Quite new, and far more rigorous conditions set in at the beginning of the older Quaternary, that is in the Pleistocene, with a very appreciable though fitful lowering of the temperature. The atmospheric precipitation became more frequent and copious; it no longer rained but snowed in the long periods of winter, and larger and larger caps accumulated. Glaciers grew and descended deep below the snowline and extended far to the south. They crossed the seas, engulfed both hills and plains, destroying all life in their slow, cold progress. They lowered the heights, deepened the valleys, crushed the obstacles which stood in their path, and dragged along the shattered fragments of rocks, and heaped them up in moraines. With the sharp edges of torn-off boulders they cut deep grooves into the rocks across which they crept towards their far-away destination, as if they wished the direction of their migration to be remembered for ever.

This huge Pleistocene glaciation was of two kinds: inland ice in the northern and central parts of the continents of the northern hemisphere, and mountain glaciation. The same was the case in the southern hemisphere. In Europe the northern inland ice spread from the Scandinavian mountains in all directions. At the time of its maximum expansion it covered the whole of Fennoscandia; to the northeast it stretched across the Urals to the river Ob, where it united with the North Siberian ice sheet. To the southeast it extended as far as the river Volga, to Kiev, and thence to Galicia, to Przemyszl, to the Beskydy, where one tongue reached into the Moravian Gate; it extended along the foot of the Sudet mountains to the Harz, the lower Rhine, and thence to Britain, which, except for the southernmost tip, it covered entirely; from Britain it extended via Iceland to Greenland. At the time of its maximum spread the area of this northern ice sheet was immense: it amounted to more than 6,000,000 square kilometres. In North America another northern ice sheet covered almost the whole of Canada, part of Alaska, and penetrated deep into the United States, to the rivers Ohio and Missouri. Its area is estimated at more than ten million square kilometres, and the thickness of the ice sheet was enormous; it is estimated at 80,000 to 90,000 feet, figures which give us some idea of the extent of the destruction wrought by this ice.

The glaciation was so big in the southern hemisphere that the rock substratum hardly rose above the surface of the ice. Vast ice masses covered the southern part of the Andes, especially in Patagonia. In the west the ice masses descended from the ridges of the Andes to the coast of the Pacific in Chile, and in the East it descended into the Argentine pampas. In Peru and Bolivia the Andes were also covered with large mountain glaciers.

The mountain glaciers increased in size on the summits of the high mountains in the northern hemisphere. Thus for instance at the time of their maximum extension the Alpine glaciers reached to the foot of the Black Forest and to the upper Danube. The Pyrenees, the Bohemian Forest, the Giant Mountains, the Caucasus, and other mountain ranges were all at that time heavily glaciated.

In these conditions it was only certain parts of Europe, especially its western, central, southeastern and eastern parts, which remained free of ice.

Before this white or bluish ice desert, life struggled for existence in the worst possible conditions, but these did not last long. The ice sheets gradually began to retreat to the north, the mountain glaciers which had crept down from the summits of the mountains to their foothill regions shrank back to the heights, and the soil, liberated from its icy cover, decked itself again in a new green robe of plants. But the northern ice-sheets resumed their attack on the southern region, again the mountain glaciers descended implacably into the valleys and foothill regions, again life was blotted out and destroyed. Then there followed another retreat of the ice, and again a new attack. This repeated itself several times. Thus the Ice Age did not form any continuous period. The *ice ages proper*, the so-called glacial periods, with a low temperature and abundant precipitation, alternated with warmer periods, the so-called *interglacial periods*, in some of which there was even in Europe a warmer climate than today. In the interglacial periods a rise in temperature melted the glaciers, and they retreated either northwards or towards the summits of the mountains. Penck and Brückner have established four glacial periods in the Alps, naming them after four small Alpine streams: Günz (the oldest), Mindel, Riss and Würm (the youngest), the three interglacial periods being known as the Günz-Mindel, the Mindel-Riss, and the Riss-Würm respectively. After the last (Würm) glacial period followed the *postglacial period*, which began about 20,000 years ago. At that time the northern ice sheet had reached in its retreat approximately the present south coast of the Baltic. The Older Quaternary, the Pleistocene, ends with the beginning of the postglacial period, and the Younger Quaternary, the Holocene, begins then.

The alternation of glacial and interglacial had a great influence on the flora of the various regions. At the onset of the Ice Ages the thermophile plant species retreated to the south or descended from the mountains into the valleys and foothills; in the interglacial periods they again returned to the north or ascended to the mountain summits.

In the glacial periods the regions which were covered by the ice were without any vegetation at all. In the periglacial regions, that is to say in the regions 125 to 185 miles in front of the northern ice sheet, there were three characteristic zones of vegetation, the tundra, the steppe, and the taiga.

At the rim of the dying glaciers, where from thousands of springs poured the turbid water of the melting ice, a flora grew up which today is found in the vast *tundras* of the northernmost parts of Europe, Asia and North America. The plants belonging to this flora were not afraid of long winters and bitter frosts, the most representative of them being various species of mosses and lichens, especially the reindeer-moss (*Cladonia rangiferina*, a lichen) and the large flat cushions of *Dryas octopetala;* in summer their white flowers made them look as if they were small green carpets densely sprinkled with snowflakes, or as if a flock of white butterflies had settled on them. With the dryads there flowered saxifrages (*Saxifraga oppositifolia*) and dwarf azaleas (*Azalea procumbens*). Various species of dwarf willows with recumbent stems formed dense growths. Thus for instance the dwarf willow (*Salix herbacea*), also today the smallest of all shrubs, formed small growths, often not more than three inches high; their trailing stems carried only two or four small green leaves, which were rounded and toothed. The stems of these tiny willows, together with stems of dwarf birch (*Betula nana*), were hardly lifted above the surface of the wet soil, yet with lichens and peat-mosses, they covered the very banks even of the snow pools and glacier streams. Towards the south the tundra passed slowly into grassy steppe. From the thick growth of the most diverse grasses rose shrubs of willows and birches, junipers and magnificently-flowering heaths; here and there grew also dwarf forms of pines (*Pinus montana* and *Pinus silvestris*). Beyond the steppe, with its cool and dry climate, stretched in a warmer and moister climate the taiga, characterised by coniferous and deciduous forests.

Whenever the ice retreated to the north, and the temperature rose, a thermophile flora again immigrated from the south, to which it had been driven by the cold and frosty breath of the ice. The types of the northern flora retreated then, together with the ice, to the north (or, in the case of the mountain glaciers, the alpine types of the flora to the summits of the mountains). This repeated cycle of glacial and interglacial periods had a great influence on the flora, owing to the alternate immigration of warmth-loving and cold-loving types from the south to north and from north to south. The remnants of the Tertiary flora, except for rare relics, became extinct during these repeated migrations, as for instance in Central Europe, or they emigrated once and for all to the European south.

When we trace the transition from the flora of a glacial period to the flora of an interglacial period, we see that this took place gradually. In some European sections of interglacial deposits, we find that above layers with a typical tundra flora there follow first deposits characterised by remains of a flora of tree-growths of pines (*Pinus silvestris*) and birches (*Betula alba*). Later these are joined by spruces (*Picea excelsa*) and firs (*Abies pectinata*) and from among deciduous trees by the poplar (*Populus tremula*). In the further development there then follows a deciduous forest with rich undergrowth, which represents in Central Europe the climax of the interglacial rise of temperature. Among the trees composing these forests may be mentioned especially oaks (*Quercus robur* and *Quercus sessilifera*), beeches (*Fagus silvatica*), lime-trees (*Tilia platyphyllos* and *Tilia parviflora*), maples (*Acer platanoides*, *Acer pseudoplatanus* and *Acer campestre*), ash-trees (*Fraxinus excelsior*), hornbeam (*Carpinus betulus*), alders (*Alnus glutinosa*), hazel (*Corylus avellana*), hawthorn (*Crataegus oxyacantha*), and others. With the onset of a new glacial period first the oak and beech forests disappeared, then the spruce, pine and birch forests, and the whole development again ended with the setting-in of a tundra flora.

In some interglacial periods certain regions, for instance in Central Europe, had among their flora plant species which no longer grow in these regions today, or which have maintained themselves in their wild form much farther south, in Southern Europe, in the Caucasus, or in Southeastern Asia. Such plant species are the Nyphaeacea (*Brasenia purpurea*), the maple (*Acer tataricum*), the rhododendron (*Rhododendron ponticum*), the box (*Buxus sempervirens*), the walnut (*Junglans regia*), the fig-tree (*Ficus carica*). Some species which were very abundant in the interglacial periods—say, in Central Europe—are very rare in these regions today, such as the water-soldier (*Stratiotes aloides*), the water-nut (*Trapa natans*), the yew (*Taxus baccata*) and others.

We can discover the same migrations of the plant associations due to the alternation of glacial and interglacial periods in the Pleistocene of North America. Nevertheless there is one great difference between the migrations of the floras of Europe and of North America, due to the different orographical conditions in the two continents. In North America the migration (from north to south in the glacial periods and from south to north in the interglacial periods) was much easier for the plants than in Europe, as all the principal North American mountain ranges (the Cordilleras, the Rocky Mountains, the Appalachian Mountains) have a meridional trend, and thus left the road open for the migrating flora. In Europe on the contrary all the main mountain systems (the Pyrenees, the Alps, the Carpathians and others) have a more or less east-west trend, and therefore constituted a considerable obstacle for the migration of the Pleistocene flora.

When after the last glacial period (Würm), the postglacial period set in some 20,000 years ago, and together with it, as we said above, the younger period of the Quaternary, the Holocene, the northern ice sheet gradually retreated from the south coast of the Baltic, farther and farther to the north, until finally it split into two small separate ice caps at Ragunda in the Scandinavian mountains. With its retreat, which had several characteristic stages, the tundras disappeared from Europe, and the steppes were quickly overgrown with thickets and woods, which became in the course of time vast, endless forests penetrating also far to the north. Europe and other regions thus gradually acquired the vegetation and the climate which they have today.

THE PRIMORDIAL HISTORY OF THE ANIMALS

Unlike plants, animals cannot nourish themselves autotrophically, and hence they could not and did not appear until after the first vegetable types. Their evolutionary history therefore also begins a little later than that of plants.

THE FIRST BEGINNINGS

Our knowledge of the earliest fauna and its initial development is but small. In the Archeozoic rocks we have not as yet really found animal remains, but, after all, this only bears out the conception which we have formed of the very first evolutionary epochs of our Earth as being without life, which appeared much later. Therefore we designate the *Archeozoic age* from this point of view also as *Azoic*, i.e. the *age without plants and animals*. From what has been said above, however, it is clear that this name is not quite correct, as already in the so-called primordial ocean period towards the end of the Archeozoic life arose and at once started to develop. Even though we do not find distinct remains of living beings in the upper Archeozoic sediments, that does not entitle us to take the term Azoic literally.

In fact, there exist certain indirect proofs that some types of organisms already existed in the upper Archeozoic. Let us remember for instance the graphite seam in the Finnish and Russian Archeozoic. We have already referred to this in connection with the origin and evolution of the algae on p. 19. We do not know any real remains of living beings from the Archeozoic. The things formerly described as remains of Archeozoic organisms have proved, in the light of modern science, to be mostly pseudo-fossils or at least problematical.

We do not find the first distinct and indubitable remains of an organic nature until the *Proterozoic* (or also Eozoic, or Algonkian), that is to say until the *age of the first antique life* or the *age of the dawn of life*. As might be expected in remains from deposits as early as this, many mistakes in identification have been made. Of what was considered the richest Proterozoan fauna, the deposits in the region of the Great Lakes in Canada, a number of hitherto cited remains have had to be crossed off the list of species by modern science. Such names as *Chuaria*, *Aspidella*, *Beltina*, *Cryptozoon*, *Carelozoon*, *Protadelaides* and others must now be relinquished. But we do know that at that time there already existed Protozoans, which we can recognize in the possible remains of Radiolarians found in France and Czechoslovakia; Proterozoic sponges have been found in France and North America, and the remains of Coelenterates from that time in England, South-west Africa and South Australia. In North America and Finland there were Proterozoic worms (*Planolites*) which left behind not only the remains of their bodies but also their trails and worm-tubes in the mud for us to find as fossils. Finally, rare finds of Brachiopods, Echinoderms, and perhaps Arthropods occasionally occur in Proterozoic deposits. We have not hitherto had any well-authenticated finds of Arthropods.

It is certain that the Proterozoic fauna was much richer and more diverse than this survey shows. As we find among it, even at this stage, remains of highly-organised invertebrates (as crustaceans and other arthropods and echinoderms), we may safely assume that in the Proterozoic the evolution of animals had gone an immensely long way, and that today we see only a section of the last act of this Proterozoic evolution. We may infer the diversity and wealth of the Proterozoic fauna also from the fact that at the very beginning of the following geological epoch, the Paleozoic, we encounter in the Cambrian seas all the animal phyla mentioned above in such a multiplicity of forms that we have to assume the preceding evolution was of long duration.

It has frequently been asked why we know so little about the living beings of the Proterozoic. The metamorphism of the rocks no longer played such an important role as in earlier ages. Clarke assumes that the main reason is that most of the Proterozoic organisms lacked a firm protective cover or supporting skeleton. Sederholm on the contrary maintains that the Proterozoic sea had a greater content of carbon dioxide so that the calcareous shells, carapaces and skeletons of the organisms dissolved after death much more quickly than in later times and today. Neither of these explanations, nor any of the others put forward, is satisfactory, however, and as yet we do not know the reason why we find so few fossils in the Proterozoic rocks.

The Proterozoic animals are interesting not only for their primitive character but also because we find among them types without even a distant analogy to known organisms. Thus in the Ediacara region, some 280 miles from Adelaide in Australia, apart from the remains of medusae *(Beltanella, Medusina, Cyclomedusa,* etc.) and worms *(Dickinsonia, Spriggina)* other types were found (such as the shield-like *Parvicorine,* evidently with appendages, and the unusual three-lobed symmetrical *Tribranchidium,* with three antenna-like tentacles), which have no equivalent in the extinct or recent animal kingdom. *Xenusion* is another strange type; it was found in the Pleistocene waste at Heiligengrabe in Germany. The quartzite pebble in which these puzzling remains were found is probably of Proterozoic age. Pompeckij, who also studied this find, compared it with trilobites, annelid worms, myriapods, crustaceans and other groups, but did not dare to place it even provisionally in any of them. The occurrence of these strange primitive types, to which we do not find any later analogy, and of others, the so-called *collective types* (i.e. types in which characters of two or more different groups occur together), should not, however, cause any particular surprise. We must not forget that these types derive from a time when the evolution of the invertebrates diverged in all directions, and expanded greatly to form the beginnings of the most diverse groups of animals, of which only those maintained themselves which by their body organisation and adaptability proved capable of further evolution and expansion. These collective types are of course not confined to the Proterozoic fauna; they also occur later, and always at a time when a sudden, rapid and richly-ramified evolution set in for a certain animal phylum or group.

Though the Proterozoic is the oldest fauna on our Earth, yet it is so only in a *temporal* sense, not in an *evolutionary* sense. The Proterozoic animals, showing already a great diversity and multiplicity, still have behind them an extremely long evolution from the primordial types, whose origin and first expansion must have taken place as far back as the end of the Archeozoic.

The expansion of the Proterozoic fauna did not, however, proceed evenly and quietly during the whole of this period, during which a sudden deterioration of the living conditions took place owing to a change of climate. A very great lowering of the average temperature set in over the whole Earth, which passed for the first time through a kind of ice age. According to many paleontologists, this climatic change had grave consequences for the expanding Proterozoic life, as it took a heavy toll of it. All the highly specialised types were unable to adapt themselves sufficiently quickly to the change and very soon died out. Only the unspecialised types maintained themselves, as they were evolutionally still sufficiently plastic to be able to react quickly to the deterioration of their environment and to maintain their existence by adaptation. It was the first time that many evolutionary branches and twigs withered on the luxuriantly budding tree of life. But those which remained developed further and became the parent stock of all other animals, and successfully expanding in later ages, many of them still live today in their distant and changed descendants.

IN THE CAMBRIAN SEAS

The manifold life in the Proterozoic seas is still lost in the misty veils of the primordial past, and our present lack of knowledge is such that we know only an insignificant fragment of it; but scant though that fragment is, it is sufficient to convince us that, at that time life had already greatly expanded, and that even now the first evolution of the invertebrates had been completed in its main lines. From the oldest Paleozoic seas, from the *Cambrian* seas, we possess so many remains of this life that we are able to visualise it clearly to ourselves. The cause of the Cambrian multiplicity of living beings is perhaps connected with the great orogenetic upheaval which took place at the end of the Proterozoic. After this upheaval new and in some ways more favourable living conditions set in. Life again altered swiftly in its endeavour to achieve balance with its environment, and as the living conditions were favourable this time, it changed and developed quickly in all directions. This is the reason why all the main groups of animals (except the vertebrates) are already represented from the time of the oldest Cambrian seas. One of the most famous localities of the Cambrian fauna is that of the fine Middle Cambrian shales discovered in 1910 by C. Walcott at Field in British Columbia. Here Walcott found seventy genera and one hundred and thirty species of uniquely well preserved fossils. The find was truly sensational, especially owing to the magnificently preserved imprints of the thalluses, of even the most delicate algae, beautifully-preserved imprints of the bodies of various medusas, worms, often with a distinct feeding tube (*Ottoia*), phyllopod crustaceans with tentacles and ribs (*Waptia*), etc.; many of these fossils suggesting masterly specimen preparation. Some of the species found have maintained themselves almost unchanged to this day; e.g. *Ayshaia* is the precursor of the present Peripatus, *Amiskwia* of the present Sagitta. But other countries are also famous for finds of Cambrian fauna, as for instance Britain, France, Germany and Czechoslovakia.

The trilobites constituted a characteristic element of the Cambrian seas; at the first glance they show a resemblance to the crustaceans, with which they were also classed until quite recently. As, however, they differ from the latter in the structure of the branched legs, they are placed today in the separate group of the Trilobitomorpha, which, together with the Chelicerata, forms the separate subphylum called Arachnomorpha (i.e. spider-like). They did not so much swim in the sea as crawl about on the bottom or in the mud of the bottom, where they searched for small animals or merely dead organic matter; therefore they are sometimes also called 'the scavengers of the sea bottom'. We know them in many genera and species (*Olenellus*, *Paradoxides*, *Ellipsocephalus*, *Olenus*, *Dicelocephalus*, etc.). The Trilobites belong also to those rare fossil animals which we know from the egg stage to the adult stage; this so-called ontogenetic development is known in a number of species, and it was first described by Barrande in the species *Sao hirsuta* from the Cambrian of Central Bohemia.

Another characteristic element of the Cambrian seas is afforded by the lamp-shells or brachiopods, whose body lay hidden inside two unequal valves, the dorsal and the ventral; their name is derived from the two arms transformed into antennae with which they guided the food to their mouths and with which they also breathed. The inequality of the valves and their symmetry (passing through the apex and centre of the valves) make them easy to distinguish from the bivalves or lamellibranchia. Most of the Cambrian brachiopods had valves of a horny substance strengthened by calcium phosphate and without a hinge. The shape of the valves of these rather primitive species greatly resembles that of the still-living genera *Discina* and *Lingula*. Among the characteristic Cambrian genera may specially be mentioned *Obolus*, *Lingulella*, *Jamesella*.

But other animals made their home in the Cambrian seas. There were notably different sponges, chiefly types with siliceous skeletal spicules; in contrast to the recent siliceous sponges, which live in the cold waters of the depths of the sea, they lived in marine shallows made light and warm by the rays of the sun. Various worms lived in the mud, colonies of so-called Archaeocyathidae covered the rocky bottom. The Archaeocyathidae lived only in those seas, and they show similarities to the calcareous sponges as well as to the Coelenterata, the corals; from calcium carbonate they built simple calyces with a cavity for the animal. We know thick layers of archaeocyathina limestones from North America, western Siberia, and Australia. In these seas the lamellibranchs and gastropods were only at the beginning of their development. Among the cephalopods of prey appeared the first Tetrabranchiata (four-gilled), the first primeval nautiloid types, especially the rather enigmatic *Volborthella*. *Hyolithus* was fairly abundant; its three-sided shells with lids often densely cover the bedding planes of some of the Cambrian shales; formerly it was placed among the Pteropoda, today rather in a separate, extinct group of molluscs. Among the Echinoderms the extinct Cystoidea were important; they are characterised by a bag- or disc-shaped shell composed of numerous immovable and irregular plates, often also with a short stem and thin arms.

IN THE ORDOVICIAN SEAS

Life in the *Ordovician seas* was still more manifold than in the Cambrian seas. Many groups of invertebrates reached the culmination of their development here, others began to expand for the first time. At the end of the Ordovician, evolution had progressed so far that the first primeval vertebrates appeared in the sea.

Among the echinoderms the Cystoidea (*Mitrocystella*, *Dendrocystites*, *Aristocystites*, *Echinosphaerites*, etc.) reached the climax of their expansion. For the first time crinoids appeared more abundantly, developing presumably from their cystoidean ancestors. Even though in these seas they were not yet nearly so widely distributed and divided into so many magnificent species as in the later seas, they were already an ornament of the Ordovician seas. Their body, covered with plates neatly arranged in a circle, was attached to the bottom by a long movable stem composed of a great number of annular segments (columnals). The mouth was framed by a wreath of movable arms, which sometimes also ramified. The crinoids mostly formed very beautiful clumps. When we try to imagine what it must have looked like when a swarm of transparent medusas with their bell-shaped or cap-shaped bodies, adorned with dozens of arms or ribbony appendages, swam above the calyx-shaped crinoids, which were not unlike huge flower buds waving on their long stems, then we must say that beauty was also born then, and that it has existed on our Earth. The brachiopods also expanded into a number of new families, genera and species, and in the more recent Ordovician seas forms with calcareous valves and a hinge predominated (*Clitambonites*, *Porambonites*, *Orthis*, etc.). The lamellibranchs and gastropods attained great generic and specific multiplicity. In the Ordovician seas occurred the first expansion of the Tetrabranchiata (four-gilled cephalopods), characterised by chambered shells; all are primitive Nautilidae, whose first tentative beginning took place in the Cambrian seas (*Volborthella*), and whose last surviving type is the modern *Nautilus* with about four species living in fairly deep waters in the Indian Ocean. The shells of the Ordovician nautilids were straight and cone-shaped; the animal lived in the last (body) chamber; the other chambers, separated by septa, were filled with air or gas, and thus the whole shell served as a hydrostatic apparatus. Each septum was perforated by a small opening with a tube-like elongation through which the special string-like body-process, the so-called siphuncle, passed to the apex of the shell; we do not as yet know for certain what was the function of this siphuncle, but it seems to have served as a firm connection of the animal to the shell, and perhaps it also made it possible for the animal to guide its movements. The nautilids are beasts of prey, and at this time their Ordovician representatives (*Endoceras*, *Orthoceras*, etc.) began to plunder the sea. The trilobites, varying in size and in the form of their bodies, also reached the climax of their development in the Ordovician seas (*Asaphus*, *Illaenus*, *Cyclopyge* with excessively-developed eyes, *Dalmanitina*, *Selenopeltis* with enormous spines on their head and body segments, etc.).

The graptolites appeared for the first time in the Ordovician seas. They are characterised by their rapid development, and at the same time (as plankton) by their wide distribution. They formed shrubby or ribbon-like colonies, which in one group (Dendroidea) were directly attached to floating tufts of algae (or more rarely to various other substrata on the bottom); in another group (Graptoloides) they floated near the surface by means of special swimming bladders or were attached to tufts of algae by a long filament. The tiny individual animals lived in tubular chambers of flexible chitin. The colony grew from the original individual, the so-called sicula, by budding. Formerly the graptolites were classed with the Coelenterata. In accordance with the investigations of the Polish paleontologist Roman Kozłowski we place them today in the family of the Pterobranchia, which, together with the Enteropneusta, form in many respects the highest organised group (Hemichordata) of the invertebrates. The graptolites became extinct before the end of the Paleozoic; nevertheless the fauna of today contains types which belong to distantly-related branches of them, as for instance *Rhabdopleura normani* from the North Sea. The older types of graptolites had shrub-like colonies. In the course of their evolution the branches were gradually reduced to two, which at the end of the filament, called nema, diverged sideways to form a fork. Still later these branches bent upwards in the direction towards the filament, until finally they enclosed the filament. Thus arose the so-called two-rowed (diplograptid) types. Still later (in the Silurian) one series of sheaths vanished, and thus the so-called uniserial (monograptid) types arose, with which the graptolites died out. Only the shrub-like and cone-shaped forms of dendroids persisted into the Carboniferous. The following species living in the Ordovician seas are of importance: *Dichograptus* with eight branches, *Tetragraptus* with four branches, *Didymograptus* with two branches in the shape of a fork, *Dicellograptus* with two branches bent upwards, *Phyllograptus* with four mutually-intergrown branches, *Diplograptus* (biserial) and others.

The Sea-mats or Bryozoa, form another new group of Ordovician fauna which has maintained itself on Earth in a great multiplicity of forms to this day. Some of them developed into beautiful colonies which look like fine regular network, and to which the old quarrymen of Central Bohemia gave the descriptive name of "lace".

Corals (Anthozoa), belonging to three different groups, were important new arrivals in the Ordovician fauna. The first of these groups was that of the Tetracoralla, which became characteristic for all later Paleozoic seas, in which they played the same role as did later the Hexacoralla, which developed from them, and which took their place in the first Mesozoic seas, surviving till today. The difference between these two groups is chiefly that while the Tetracoralla have their septa and tentacles based on the number four, the Hexacoralla have theirs based on the number six. They were solitary or formed colonies. The Tabulata always formed colonies of the most diverse shapes, in which each animal made for itself a firm calcareous shell divided by numerous transverse septa, the so-called plates (tabulae). The third group of corals in the Ordovician seas includes the so-called Heliolitidae, members of the Octocoralla, likewise forming colonies of various shapes, often several feet in diameter. All these corals formed dense growths (biohermae) on suitable places on the floor of the sea and sometimes they give the impression of being coral reefs; the resemblance is, however, only superficial.

The most important feature of the Ordovician seas from the point of view of the history of evolution is, however, the fact that it was in the late Ordovician that the earliest jawless vertebrates, the Agnathi, made their appearance. We shall revert to them below.

IN THE SILURIAN SEAS

A great expansion of the invertebrates took place in the Silurian seas, and its special feature was that animals with calcareous shells or skeletons developed.

The explosive and many-sided expansion occurred first of all among the corals, trilobites, lamellibranchia, gastropods, brachiopods, cephalopods, crinoids, etc. Here and there the crinoids were so abundant that they formed large, magnificent clumps; after their death their bodies fell to pieces and the freed plates of their calyces and the annular columnals of their stems today compose many limestone beds. The brachiopods lived here, too, in such great quantities that certain Silurian limestones are overcrowded with their valves. The crustaceans also developed rapidly; their origin has to be sought as far back as in the Ordovician and Cambrian seas. The Arachnomorpha (spider-like arthropods) also underwent a great expansion; they belong to the group of the Xiphosura, of which the well-known king-crab *(Limulus)* survives until today as their only modern representative; in the Silurian seas they were represented for instance by

Eurypterus, whose last (sixth) pair of legs was transformed into powerful rowing organs; by *Pterygotus*, whose second pair of limbs was transformed into powerful claws; by *Carcinosoma*, similar to a scorpion, and with a sharp, sword-like curved point (presumably with a poison gland) at the end of the body; and also the giant *Stylonurus* growing to as much as ten feet. All these and many other sea-scorpions were formidable beasts of prey in the Silurian seas.

While these groups flourished in the Silurian seas, others, as for instance the Cystoidea, retired into the background.

But what is from the evolutionary viewpoint the most important and the most remarkable feature of the Silurian period is that it was in these ancient seas that the *earliest primitive jawless vertebrates* similar to the fish appeared in great numbers. This really marked a great step forward, as it was the first appearance of a higher type than even the most highly-organised invertebrates of the previous period; it was the appearance of the type which, from such modest and inconspicuous beginnings, pressed unceasingly forward and upward, until finally it ended with the mammals and with man himself. It is worth while for us to dwell on it a little.

THE CRADLE OF THE EARLIEST VERTEBRATES

The *Silurian waters* are memorable for the appearance of the earliest vertebrates.

We do not know as yet much about the origin and initial development of the vertebrates. Though several, and often very clever, theories have been advanced to account for this origin, yet so far we are positive about nothing. What we do know is that these earliest primitive jawless vertebrates resembled fishes and did not occur in any abundance until the Silurian, although their first representatives (*Astraspis desiderata* and *Eriptychius americanum*) have been found in the Upper Ordovician beds of North America. If therefore these primitive vertebrates appeared with their rare first types already fully evolved in the Upper Ordovician beds, then we must trace their origin to some primeval chordates, whose only, but according to W. K. Gregory very changed, representative today is the lancelet (*Amphioxus*); their initial development must thus have taken place at least in the Cambrian seas, if not even in the Proterozoic seas. W. K. Gregory calls these early chordates 'the basic chordates'.

We class all these primitive Agnatha in the group of the *Ostracodermi*. They had an inner cartilaginous skeleton, and a firm outer carapace composed of bone plates and shields, forming a case for the head and more than half the interior part of the body; only the caudal part of the body was free. Paired limbs were lacking, and the acoustic (or rather static) organ is marked only by two semicircular canals. Their most important feature is, however, that they lack the lower jaw. In a number of these features they closely approach the recent Cyclostomata ('round-mouths'), with which they have in common a very similar brain structure, whereas they are strikingly distinguished from all other vertebrates, especially from the fish; therefore we combine the Ostracodermi and the Cyclostomata in the group of the Agnathi, which is taxonomically equivalent to the group of the Gnathostomata, to which all the other vertebrates belong, i.e. fishes, amphibians, reptilians, birds, and mammals.

Both W. K. Gregory and E. A. Stensiö, the great Swedish paleontologist who has contributed so much to our knowledge of primitive Agnathi, assume their ancestors to have been not only naked but transparent, and we may well wonder how it was that from these transparent animals such heavily armoured types developed. Homer Smith explained it as the consequence of their descendants having passed from the sea into fresh water. The difference in the concentration of the salts in the fresh water and in the blood of these descendants he takes to have been so great that the percolation of water into the body threatened to produce dangerous swellings and tumours, and that against this they protected themselves by the formation of a firm external skeleton. Gregory rightly points out, however, that there is no proof that the Ostracodermi derive from the primary marine chordates, but that on the contrary they may derive from primary fresh-water chordates. Thus the question remains open.

The Ostracodermi are divided into several groups according to the structure and arrangement of the bone armour. It is interesting to note that already at the end of the Silurian there appeared several forms with thinner and lighter armour (e.g. *Phlebolepsis*), and even forms which completely lacked an external skeleton (e.g. *Jaymotius kerwoodi*, in which Gregory sees the immediate ancestor of Amphioxus). The transition between the heavily-armoured forms and the forms without an outer skeleton was thus gradual. The main evolution of the Ostracodermi occurred in the Silurian seas; they were on the decline in the Devonian seas and then became extinct. We know many different genera (*Pteraspis, Drepanaspis, Cephalaspis, Birkenia, Lanarkia, Thelodus*, etc.). We know also genera (*Kiaeraspis*) which had electric organs, serving not only for their protection but also for stunning or killing their victims.

The Ostracodermi are of great evolutionary importance. Not only did they become the ancestors of a further, higher group of vertebrates, the so-called Placodermi, a kind of primary fish from which all other fish can be derived, but they are also the distant ancestors of the present Cyclostomata, which, because of their parasitic life, change, however, into simpler types, characterised chiefly by the complete loss of their armour.

IN THE DEVONIAN SEAS

If in the Silurian seas the way was prepared for fauna of more modern character than in earlier times, the fauna of the *Devonian seas* was simply the fulfilment of this promise. Here almost all groups of vertebrates were already represented, so that further evolution in later geological ages, the unceasing adaptation and perfection of more modern and higher types, and of course parallel with this the dying out of old-fashioned and more primitive types, only supplemented the different groups, families and genera. Yet in the Devonian waters two newcomers to the animal complex appeared.

The first appearance of a new group of tetrabranchiate cephalopods, the so-called goniatites, is important among the invertebrates. In the goniatites the chambered, coiled and usually disc-shaped shell has zigzag septal sutures. The first Goniatidae, which appeared as early as the boundary of the Silurian and the Devonian, probably originated from nautiloid ancestors among the Silurian genus *Protobactrites*. It was not, however, until the later Carboniferous seas that, through the growing complexity of the suture line and its lobes, the first ammonites developed from them. The ammonites were widely distributed in all the Mesozoic seas and are very typical of them.

The Devonian age with its waters is, however, especially important, because it was then that the *great expansion of the fishes* took place; therefore the Devonian age is sometimes also called the *age of the fishes*. The oldest and most important of these fishes from the point of view of evolution are the so-called *Placodermi:* they were armoured fishes, which in the development of the vertebrates represent a higher stage than that of the Silurian Ostracodermi. Though their first appearance actually occurred in Upper Silurian waters, yet their chief expansion and flourishing took place in the Devonian waters; in the Carboniferous their last representatives became completely extinct. The Placodermi have a higher organisation than the Ostracodermi. They have paired nasal openings, at least one pair of bony and articulated thoracic limbs, and —most important—they have, like all other vertebrates, two jaws moving against each other, which represent the highly evolved gill-arches. According to W. K. Gregory, we have to seek the ancestors of the Placodermi among the Ostracodermi, among the Cephalaspidi. The armoured fishes, which because of their primitive appearance and their many primitive features are designated by some paleontologists as armoured primordial fishes, lived in the Devonian waters, i.e. in the seas of coastal lagoons, in fresh-water swamps and in the wide river-mouths of the so-called Northern Old Red Continent. The continent arose owing to the extensive uplift during the Caledonian orogeny at the end of the Silurian, and in the Devonian. These fishes occurred in small (*Coccosteus, Pterichthys*, most Acanthodidi) and large genera (*Macropetalichthys, Titanichthys, Dinichthys*). Evolutionally the Placodermi are of the greatest importance, as all other groups of fishes developed from them. Thus for instance from the Macropetalichthydi (which had only the head protected by armour, whereas the body was naked, and which already had a double olfactory nerve) there developed the first fishes of the sub-class of sharks (Elasmobranchii, Selachii, the Devonian *Cladoselache*), while from the Acanthodidi developed the ancestor of the spine-finned fishes (Acanthopterygii, the Devonian *Cheirolepis*), etc.

With the armoured fishes the wealth of Devonian fishes is not, however, exhausted. Together with them lived the first sharks, the first bony fishes, and especially also the first Dipnoi (lung-fishes), and Crossopterygii (lobe-fins). We shall return to the last two below.

THE ATTACK OF THE ANIMALS ON THE LAND

We know already that at the end of the Silurian and the beginning of the Devonian the plants finally conquered the dry land and began to develop, according to the character of their environment, into a number of different types. This conquest gave the first and basic condition for the origin and development of a *land fauna*. So long as the continent was desert, so long as it was covered only by a desolate waste of sand or jagged barren rocks, aquatic fauna, whether marine or freshwater, could never succeed in conquering the dry land. Every attempt was foredoomed to failure because of the lack of food. But as soon as patches of green vegetation relieved the barrenness of the dry land, the most varied animal types could inhabit these early sites; they lived on the tissues of the plants, whether living or already dead and rotting.

It is a matter for regret that we do not yet know in what manner the animals conquered the dry land, and which animal type it was which first succeeded in doing so. There is no reason to doubt that they belonged to the invertebrates, although the remains which we have of them from the end of the Silurian and from the Devonian are too few to enable us to settle the point. According to our present knowledge the oldest animals of the dry land included the myriapods and scorpions (Devonian myriapods: *Archidesmus* and *Kampecaris* from Scotland, and Upper Silurian scorpions: *Palaeophonus* and *Proscorpius* from the island of Gotland), to which we have to add, according to recent finds, the wingless insects, whose remains were found in the Devonian of Scotland and, quite recently, also in the Devonian of Czechoslovakia, which remains have been described as *Rhyniella* and are related to the recent Collembola. All these representatives of the invertebrates conquered the dry land very soon after the oldest land plants had made their home permanently on the banks of the waters.

Although we know nothing in detail about the origin and development of the first land invertebrates, we do know something about the origin of the first land vertebrates, which made their appearance and began to develop in the Upper Devonian. This is so outstanding an event that we may well deal more specifically with it.

It is certain that the most primitive type of land vertebrates is represented by the *amphibia*, and it is also certain that they developed from the *fishes*. The question is from which fishes did they develop, how and when?

If, in our attempt to answer these questions, we turn our attention to the Devonian seas and their fishes, we find that these waters were also the cradle of that remarkable group of fishes which have gills as well as a form of lungs, and which have such striking similarities to the amphibia that at the time of their discovery they were even regarded as a king of "piscine amphibia". They are the so-called *Dipnoi* (double breathers, lung fishes), whose most important special feature is that their air bladder can function also as an auxiliary respiratory organ; hence their name. The present lung fishes (the Brazilian *Lepidosiren*, the African *Protopterus*, and the Australian *Neoceratodus*) represent only the merest remnants of this formerly multifarious group of fishes, whose beginnings reach back to the Devonian (*Dipterus*, *Conchodus*, *Holodus* and others). It was formerly thought that the first land vertebrates, the amphibian Stegocephali, developed from these fishes. The results of recent investigations have, however, shown that this is not so, and that the Dipnoi, though representing a quite special and in many respects strange group, have no special evolutionary importance.

The evolutionary importance is now thought to lie with another interesting group of fishes, the Crossopterygii. They get their name from the peculiar shape of their fins, which consist of a kind of tassel with a scaly central axis (tassel-finned). Their air bladder is able to take in atmospheric oxygen. These tassel-finned fish appeared for the first time in the Devonian waters; the most important among them is *Osteolepis*, from which several evolutionary series lead to extinct types, of which the Permian *Laugia* became the ancestor of the Cretaceous *Undina*, a direct ancestor of *Latimeria*, the recent discovery of which caused excitement in scientific circles. The expansion of the tassel-finned fishes occurs in the Devonian, Carboniferous and Permian seas; after that time they decreased considerably in importance, and nowadays we find only the last occasional remnants of this once-flourishing group of fishes (in addition to the marine genus *Latimeria* and to more lately discovered genus *Malania*. The tassel-finned fishes do not, however, include the already well-known genera *Polypterus* and *Calamichthys* from the fresh waters of Africa). These fishes are also characterised by double breathing; the walls of their air bladder are crowded with capillary blood vessels, and thus adapted to the oxidation of the blood with gaseous oxygen from the air, but not with the oxygen dissolved in the water, which is taken in with the gills. Thus the tassel-finned fishes also possess a kind of primitive lungs, and these lungs resemble those of the higher land vertebrates more closely than those of the Dipnoi.

Although the tassel-finned fishes are markedly on the decline today, this does not mean that their past was unimportant; quite the contrary, for it was one of their types which branched off as far back as the Devonian, to lead in the course of further evolution to the first land quadrupeds, the amphibian stegocephalians. At first the tassel-finned fishes, and the types of the diverging branch, lived together in the Upper Devonian lakes and swamps. The differences between them were to begin with insignificant divergences, with regard both to the shape of their body as well as to their mode of life.

Professor A. S. Romer has solved the question of the causes which led to the origin of the first amphibian from the Crossopterygii, with which they lived together. They were beasts of prey and relatively rather big. Most of their life they spent in the water. Why then did they leave it? It was certainly not in order to be able to breathe the air, for even though they may have lived in stagnant, putrid water with a lack of oxygen, they had only to rise to the surface to swallow air. Nor was it because they were forced to search for food outside the water, for the continent was at that time still fairly barren and short of animal food. Nor can the reason have been that they were threatened by some enemy, for they were at that time the most powerful animals in fresh water. Taking into consideration all these and many other possibilities, we arrive finally at the apparently paradoxical conclusion that they turned to life on the dry land in order to be able to stay in the water. The explanation of this paradox is as follows: the primitive ancestors of the stegocephalian differed very little from the Crossopterygii. The only difference between the two was that the former had their fins somewhat more strongly developed. This was both a drawback and an advantage; it was a drawback when there was much water in the lake or swamp in which they lived, as their massively-built fins were less suitable for swimming than the more lightly-built fins of the Crossopterygii. As soon, however, as the burning sun dried out the lakes and swamps and only small puddles were left, then the tassel-finned ancestors of the amphibia had the advantage, because with their more strongly-developed limbs they were better able than the tassel-finned fish to move about in the drying mud of the disappearing puddles. In fact, the latter were even threatened with death if for any reason the water did not again flood the lake or swamp. The tassel-finned ancestors of the amphibia, on the other hand, could in such a case use their ability to crawl about in the mud of the dried-up puddles or for an attempt to crawl across to another pool which still held water. Thus we arrive at the paradox that their transition to life on land was really the outcome of their endeavour to continue life in an aquatic environment. It is incontestable that the tassel-finned ancestors of the amphibia succeeded in making their way from one pool to another on dry land, being effectively helped also by the fact that they, just like the related true tassel-finned fish, had an air bladder which had already developed into a kind of primitive lung for taking in atmospheric oxygen. But these tassel-finned ancestors of the amphibia had still another advantage, which showed itself when living conditions became unfavourable. Perhaps not all of them, but at least some of them spent a certain time in the dried-out pools, so long as they had not eaten all the dead fish. Thus they lengthened their stay on dry land, and thus the transformation of their fins into limbs also took place more effectively and their body also underwent changes. It is certain that even in these early evolutionary stages some re-oriented themselves exclusively to fish-food, others to insect-food, others again exclusively to vegetables, the last especially at the time when the land vegetation had already greatly expanded, and when the swamps were fringed by large dense clumps of the tree-like lycopods and ferns, sheltering a fairly rich and diverse land fauna. These newly-developed types of amphibia lived mainly on the banks of lakes and swamps, but they never left the neighbourhood of water. Remains of these earliest amphibia, the stegocephalians, are known from as early as the end of the Devonian of North America *(Elpistostege)* and Greenland *(Ichthyostega* and *Ichthyostegopsis)*.

Thus as early as at the end of the Devonian evolution had arrived, by transforming the Crossopterygii, at the *first amphibia*. This slow transformation had come about in the following stages: (1) the transition from breathing through gills to breathing through lungs, (2) the transformation of the fin into a limb, (3) a greater mobility of the head in conjunction with a differentiation of the cervical part of the spine, (4) the origin of cranial bones, characteristic of all higher vertebrates, and finally, (5) changes in the circulation of the blood called forth by the new way of breathing. Except for the changes in the circulation of the blood, we can trace all these changes distinctly in our fossil material.

One more brief remark on the astounding transformation of fish into amphibia. We know that from the fish fin there arose, by a reduction in the number of fin rays, the primary five-fingered limb of the land quadruped. From this point of view, the human limbs are in a very primitive evolutionary stage, and the beginning of their five-fingered shape has to be sought in those ancient times at least three hundred million years ago. It would, however, be a mistake to believe that for this reason the human hand is a primitive organ; just the contrary is true. In its final organisation the human hand is a well-nigh perfect instrument, and in the words of Charles Darwin 'man could not have reached his ruling position in the world without his hand'. Thus the human hand is primitive only morphologically, not functionally.

THE AMPHIBIA RULE THE WORLD

The Carboniferous period, following upon the Devonian period with its outstanding importance from the evolutionary point of view, brought an unusually interesting expansion of the animals.

In the seas this was not so striking and marked, though there too life became very manifold. Many groups just managed to survive into the Carboniferous, others flourished. Some protozoans were very numerous, as for instance the foraminifer Fusulina, whose shells like grains of corn built whole thick beds. Primitive corals, crinoids, lamellibranchs, gastropods, brachiopods, and cephalopods were also abundant. The trilobites were on the contrary already in marked decline.

On land, however, until then so poor in life, the fauna expanded richly and in a variety of directions. The warm and moist climate, the vast primeval forests, and the abundance of water, created optimum living conditions. Various crustaceans and fishes developed greatly in the waters, while on land the first terrestrial gastropods and winged insects appeared, often of surprising size (as for instance the archaic dragon-fly *Meganeura* with a wing-span of two and a half feet, not unlike a miniature aeroplane). In the primeval Carboniferous forests this insect attained wide distribution, and it became the basis for the further development of *all* winged insects. The spiders, the centipedes and the scorpions also achieved great expansion. The stegocephalians reached the climax of their evolution. They had bodies of different sizes and shapes, some like the lizards (as *Urocordylus* and *Discosauriscus*) or salamanders of today (as *Branchiosaurus*), others like snakes (as *Dolichosoma*) or crocodiles (as *Archegosaurus*); their body was covered with an armour consisting of scales or plates. These archeamphibia were the leading animals of their time and gave it is specific character.

THE FIRST REPTILES

Primordial forests like the Carboniferous ones also grew in the Permian. But as we saw above, there was a certain change of climate in the new period. The moist and warm climate of the Carboniferous, which suited the flora, the amphibian stegocephalians, and in general all the fauna living at that time so well, began to change to a drier one even at the end of the Carboniferous and especially at the beginning of the Permian. The vast forests became less extensive as sandy wastes and deserts encroached upon them, until finally it was the latter which determined the character of the continent in Europe and elsewhere.

These profound changes in living conditions did not of course fail to have a radical influence on the evolution of the animals, especially of the vertebrates. The stegocephalians had to take refuge in the remaining swamps, which as larger or smaller green oases relieved the monotony of the sandy wastes and deserts. But some of the stegocephalians which were not as yet overspecialised, and thus capable of reacting to the changing environment, began to adapt themselves to the conditions of their surroundings, that is, to a life in drier regions. Their fine scales disappeared, and in their stead appeared a horny skin whose firm shield protected their bodies from dangerous evaporation of water. They ceased to lay eggs in the water, but instead buried them in heaps of rotting plants or directly in the sand, and while earlier the development of the embryo had taken place in the water, it now took place in a fluid contained in the so-called amnion cavity of the egg. All the higher vertebrates constituting the group Amniota, whether reptiles, birds, or mammals, have preserved this form of embryonic development till today. These and still other changes, all called forth by the change in the living conditions of the environment and by the fauna's reaction to it, resulted ultimately in the development of the *first archaic reptiles* from certain stegocephalians. Again a great forward leap had been accomplished in the evolution of the animals: the higher reptile had developed from the lower amphibian.

Though the first archaic reptiles had appeared at the end of the Carboniferous, their first expansion did not come until the Permian, when we can distinguish among them several basic evolutionary branches. Some of these developed into ponderous and clumsy animals with remarkably strong bones in their limbs and their girdles (as *Pareiosaurus*, *Moschops*, etc), others into agile and slender animals of the lizard type (as *Araeoscelis*). Certain regions of the Permian of South Africa, South America, and Russia were especially important centres for the origin and development of these strange archereptiles.

AT THE END OF THE PALEOZOIC

A very long time, some two hundred to three hundred million years, separates us from the time when the forests of the Permocarboniferous grew on our Earth, and around them barren sandy wastes and deserts extended to the horizon and beyond. These primeval jungles with sunshine, moonlight, veils of mist, crashing thunderstorms, and the beauty of the rising and setting sun, the homes of peculiar primitive flora and fauna, formed a striking contrast to the sandy wastes burned by the glare of the sun and sparsely inhabited. And when thunderstorms and whirlwinds did not rage over the forests and wastes, attended by the splintering of trunks, the snapping of branches and the swishing of sand grains driven before them, then a heavy and dead silence brooded over these regions, for there was not as yet one single bird to sing the praise of the dawning day, nor one single mammal to challenge its rival in a ringing voice to a duel. Life was still mute, for the crown of evolution was then represented only by the amphibian stegocephalian and the rare archaic reptile. No higher vertebrate type had been evolved; that was to come in the course of later ages.

Thus it was at the end of the Permian, when one of the major evolutionary stages of the animals, the Paleozoic or *Antiquity of the Animals*, came to an end. This stage is somewhat late as compared with the evolution of the plants, for while the Paleophytic, the Antiquity of the Plants, ends with the Lower Permian, the Paleozoic ends only with the Upper Permian.

THE DAWN OF THE MESOZOIC

After the end of the Paleozoic the geological ancient history of the Earth and the evolutionary ancient history of living beings continued in the *Mesozoic*, which is divided into three formations, the Triassic, the Jurassic and the Cretaceous. Dry and moist periods, swampy and desert regions, volcanic activity, minor and major inundations of the continents by the sea, all these and many other events also had a great influence on living beings and their evolution.

In the Triassic seas many groups of the most important invertebrates of the Paleozoic seas were now missing; this applies for instance to the trilobites, the Tetracoralla, which were replaced by the Hexacoralla, the graptolites and others. The crinoids were no longer so manifold in shape as before, even though some species, such as the Triassic *Encrinus liliiformis* formed here and there dense growths, from which limestones overcrowded with remains of their disintegrated skeletons later arose. Lamellibranchs, gastropods and brachiopods were, however, abundant. The most typical animals in all Mesozoic seas were the ammonites, which attained a stupendous abundance, but they all died out without leaving any descendants in the Cretaceous seas at the end of the Mesozoic. The Belemnites (two-gilled cephalopods, Dibranchiata) had a similar importance, but they, too, became extinct in the Cretaceous seas.

THE WORLD OF THE GIANT REPTILES

The most characteristic feature of the Mesozoic is the striking and surprising expansion of the reptiles; it is because of this that the Mesozoic, the *Middle Ages of the Animals*, is also called the *Age of Reptiles*.

The amphibian stegocephalians, which were so important for the Carboniferous and the Permian, were, at the very beginning of the Mesozoic, in the Triassic, in obvious decline. A multitude of them perished, and only the last remnants maintained themselves in swamps and pools, which, however, were on the whole few and of small size in the Triassic as compared with the extensive Permocarboniferous swamps. Some of the survivors of the stegocephalians attained, however, vast dimensions; a monster of this kind was for instance *Mastodonsaurus*, a stegocephalian having a body like a frog with a short tail and skull more than three feet long; it has appropriately been called the frog saurian. At the end of the Triassic the stegocephalians became completely extinct, but of course long before that they had developed more modern successors (salamanders, tritons, frogs, and Gymnophiona). These successors never attained the importance which their ancestors had had, and this is the reason why the whole of the Mesozoic became the Age of Reptiles, which typified Mesozoic life in the water, on land, and in the air. When we compare this Mesozoic reptilian world with that of today, we see that there has been a great decline of the reptilian phylum; of about twenty large groups of Mesozoic reptiles, only a few have survived till today. Different living conditions in various regions led to the most diverse modes of adaptation, and thus also to the most varied reptilian types, which often surprise us today.

Some of them lived *in the sea*. Their re-adaptation to an aquatic life was accomplished in different ways, but it was always perfect. The aquatic reptiles were beasts of prey *(Ichthyosaurus, Plesiosaurus, Mosasaurus, Tylosaurus)*, as dangerous and savage as the sharks of today. Many of them attained an extraordinary size (like the Cretaceous plesiosaurid *Elasmosaurus*, which was forty-one feet long). The Mesozoic seas were also inhabited by numerous crocodiles; the largest species of the genus *Steneosaurus* from the Jurassic seas of Europe attained a length of up to nineteen feet. Some of these Mesozoic marine crocodiles *(Metriorhynchus* and *Geosaurus)* even had their limbs transformed again into fins, which shows that they never left the water. The so-called Placodontia may be mentioned among the other Triassic reptiles; they had a short neck, a long tail, and a slender, triangular body; this strange shape was due to their unique ventral armour, which consisted of ventral ribs bent at right angles. Their mouth was filled with button-shaped teeth, with which they crushed the shells of the lamellibranchs, gastropods and brachiopods on which they lived. *Placodus*, about six feet long, is the best known of this group; the strangest of all of them is

Henodus, whose whole body was encased in a firm armour, like the tortoises of today. We are to a great extent indebted to Professor F. von Huene, of the University of Tübingen, for our knowledge of these strange reptiles. The nothosaurids, predators of the Triassic seas, were another group of reptiles which had a dragon-like appearance; *Nothosaurus mirabilis* was about ten feet long.

Among the Mesozoic reptiles which gave the continental fauna its special character were the well-known *dinosaurs*, the giant saurians. Extinct reptiles of the most varied appearance, size, and habits belong to them. They were both carnivores and herbivores; they lived in lowlands full of swamps and bogs but also in dry or desert regions. Many of them attained gigantic size (like the Jurassic *Diplodocus*, which was eighty-six feet long). Their bodies were naked or covered with strong scales. Many of them also developed an exoderm composed of strong bony plates or spines. The skull was as a rule small compared with the rest of the body; thus the brain was also small, and with this again a low mental capacity was connected. To compensate for this a second nerve centre developed in the area of the sacral vertebrae, and this was sometimes up to ten times larger than the brain itself. The remarkable swelling of the spinal cord in the area of the sacral vertebrae is certainly closely connected with the huge development of the hind-limbs, as of the tail. The giant saurians lived from the beginning of the Triassic till the end of the Cretaceous; then they became completely extinct without any living descendants.

But the reptiles also dominated the air in the Mesozoic. Theseflying reptiles were the *Pterosaurians*, which in variously-shaped genera and species cleft the tropical air. Some of them, as for instance *Pteranodon*, looked like real fairy-tale dragons of enormous size. They were excellently adapted to life in the air, and their fore-limbs were transformed into flying organs.

The origin, expansion and extinction of all these strange Mesozoic reptiles constituted only an episode in the magnificent evolution of creation on our Earth. Formerly the hope was frequently expressed that one day we might find some descendants of them in one of the unknown corners of our globe; but nowadays we know that such a hope is vain, and that they became extinct many millions of years ago.

THE TOOTHED BIRDS

In 1859, a year after the publication of Darwin's theory regarding the origin of mankind—that is at a time when the first passionate controversy about the theory of evolution had started among scientists—the news came from Solenhofen in Bavaria that a strange petrified creature had been found in the lithographic slates there, and that it represented a kind of transitional link between the reptiles and the birds. An animal had been found which was of greater importance than any other in the controversy over Darwin's theory of evolution; no better proof for his theory could well have been imagined. But the opponents of the theory of evolution made light of the find, because of the incompleteness of the skeleton, and some of them did not even hesitate to spread the malicious rumour that it might be a fake. When, however, sixteen years later in the same slates at Eichstätt another skeleton of this strange animal was discovered, this time beautifully and completely preserved, the opponents and scoffers fell silent, and many a former opponent even turned into a humble adherent of the new theory. These famous finds brought to light the *toothed bird (Archaeopteryx lithographica)*; they are perhaps the best known of all paleontological finds.

It came as a surprise to the paleontologists that in the Upper Jurassic evolution had already proceeded so far as to make the first birds appear, primitive though they were. These Upper Jurassic birds have, however, nothing whatever in common with the flying reptiles, as is often imagined even today by lay people. We have to look for the origin of these birds to another extinct reptilian group, to the Pseudosuchia, whose members lived in the Permian and in the Triassic (such as *Ornithosuchus* or *Euparkeria)*. These saurian arch-ancestors of the birds, which we do not yet know well, lived in rocky and semi-desert regions where there were many shrubs, and they seem t have gone over to walking and running on their hind-legs only. Their bodies were still covered with scales. At a further stage of evolution, for which we still have no evidence but which we must assume to have existed, the pseudosuchian saurian turned into a kind of 'pre-bird', proavis, with feathers and already able to climb about on the trunks and branches of the trees. By the transformation of its scales into feathers and at the same time by the lengthening of the feathers on the outer side of its fore-limbs and on the whole of the tail, there arose in the course of further evolution a kind of parachute, which allowed it to glide smoothly down from branch to branch and from a tree to the ground. That was the first beginning of flight, which, with the gradual transformation of the proavis into the archaic bird, and then of the archaic bird into the bird, was constantly improved.

Still another important fact is directly connected with the origin of the birds from the saurians. This is the knowledge that the continuous feather cover of the body led to the maintenance of a constant blood temperature and to the further changes of body organisation resulting from this. For the first time in the evolutionary history of the vertebrates we encounter here a type of animal with a *constant body temperature:* until then the fauna had consisted only of animals with variable temperatures (fish, amphibians and reptiles), which from the evolutionary point of view is a lower stage, as the dependence of the body temperature on the environment is certainly a very heavy handicap.

The Jurassic birds did not survive the Jurassic period. With its close they too disappeared from the surface of the Earth. The wealth and variety of the birds of later days must not lead us to underestimate their appearance, sporadic and rare though it was. On the contrary, it has to be emphasised that it is just these birds which, by their skeletons, have helped new ideas and a new theory to gain victory. This by itself should surely be a sufficient reason for never forgetting them.

THE FIRST MAMMALS

In the Mesozoic, when the reptiles took over the mastery of the world, and when they began to dominate completely land, water and air in an unending multiplicity of forms and often of amazingly large dimensions, such evolutionary transformations took place as made the whole of this monstrous reptilian world appear a small matter. It was just these most gigantic, most striking and best-known types that died out completely at the end of the Mesozoic without leaving any descendants, among other reasons because their narrow specialisation prevented them from adapting themselves to the new living conditions offered by the changing environment. They would have fallen entirely into oblivion if it were not for the paleontologists, who dig up their skeletons in inhospitable regions, describe and picture them, and write books about them. And these types which, because of their size and often also because of their bizarre appearance, have stimulated today such a great interest even among lay people, were from the evolutionary point of view really only dead ends. Though sometimes forking in many directions, they never led forwards, never became a path leading to higher types. They appeared, lived and died, and today we only stand in wonder before their skeletons.

But besides this obvious saurian world, the Mesozoic harboured still another, of much smaller dimensions, simpler in shape, and living in comparative retirement. And it was these small, inconspicuous reptiles which were sensitive to the influence of the environment, and which passed through those bodily changes which led some of their distant descendants to become the archetypes of the highest group of vertebrates, the mammals.

It was a long road, remarkably alike in its width and in its details, before the *first mammal* developed from the reptile. Before we follow this way, let us return for a while to the ages when, from the amphibian stegocephalian of the Carboniferous forests, the first reptile developed.

We have pointed out above the causes which led to the transformation of the amphibian stegocephalians into the archaic reptiles. These were especially: the decrease in the number and size of swamps and bogs, which forced the stegocephalians to concentrate in the few which remained or to adapt themselves to the increasing dryness and to life in waterless regions, to give up laying their eggs in water in which the young passed their larval development, and to find a way of laying their eggs in sand without involving the danger of extinction of the species. Even at a time when the Carboniferous forests still existed, we find in the stegocephalians the first indications of the development of a higher animal type—the reptiles. The first reptilian types and the most advanced stegocephalian types are in many respects very similar; so much so in fact that with some of them only an expert experienced in the subject can tell whether a given genus belongs to the amphibia or to the reptiles, as for instance in the case of the stegocephalian genus *Seymouria.*

The most primitive and earliest reptiles are very closely related to their stegocephalian ancestors, with which they have a whole number of features in common, for instance, the skull with the ear incisions completely closed over by bones (the so-called stegocephalian type of skull), the structure of the shoulder girdle, the one sacral vertebra, the ventral ribs, etc.

On the other hand, these reptiles exhibit great differences of form. This shows that they quickly expanded into a number of separate evolutionaty branches, many of which soon died out, while others continued further in their transformed descendants. We find among them strange, massively-built and unwieldy forms (as *Pareiosaurus*, *Moschops*, *Dimetrodon*, *Edaphosaurus*, etc.), and also smaller, less striking forms, whose significant feature was the evolutionary tendency directed towards the origin of the mammals. This tendency revealed itself especially in the morphological differentiation of the teeth and their enlargement, the gradual decrease of the various bones of the lower jaw, the change in the structure of the base of the skull, and finally also in the formation of a distinct muzzle caused by the marked narrowing of the anterior part of the skull. There was also an erection of the limbs, that is to say the humerus and femur acquired a vertical instead of a horizontal position; this also involved radical changes in the structure of the limbs themselves (especially of the anterior ones) and in the structure of the supporting girdles. This, too, shows a higher evolutionary trend. Another important change was the stabilisation of the fingers at the number of five, and of the finger joints at the number of 2, 3, 3, 3, 3. Both these features were also transmitted to, the mammals (in so far as there was not again a reduction during later development). The arrangement of the joints in our hands and feet, where the pollex always has two and the other digits three joints, is thus a permanent and unchanged inheritance from these reptiles.

All these mammalian features showed themselves most strongly in the small reptiles of the group Ictidosaurus from the Triassic, and it is also from these ictidosaurian reptiles that the first mammals originated. Great knowledge and experience are, however, needed in order to be able to class the most highly organised ictidosaurian reptiles and the most primitive mammals in the groups to which they belong, as they are indeed surprisingly similar to each other.

Together with the morphological transformation of the reptile into the mammal went other changes which, though we cannot observe them in the skeletal remains, we have to assume; of these changes warm-bloodedness is the most important, with all the differences it involved in the circulation of the blood; and next in importance comes the origin of the milk-glands, so characteristic of the mammals; this change was again closely connected with the new system of embryonic development, i.e. with the transition from the freely-laid reptilian egg warmed mainly by the heat of the sun, to eggs warmed by the warmth of the mother as in the Monotremata, and finally to development in the maternal womb and to viviparity.

From what has been said above it will be gathered that the ancestors of the mammals are not to be found among the monstrous and giant reptilian forms; they were but the extravagant aberrations of a hasty development. On the contrary, it was the small and unobtrusive reptiles of the Ictidosaurids (*Dromatherium*, *Microconodon*, *Microleptes*, *Tritolodon*, etc.) that became the ancestors of the mammals which after the reptiles ruled the world and among which is to be sought the origin of man himself, the ruler and master of nature.

ON THE THRESHOLD OF THE TERTIARY

Early dawn began to spread its grey veil over the earth preparatory to chasing the night. From the horizon in the east it painted the sky gold and vermilion, and after a while the sun appeared. Thousands of dewdrops on the shadowy earth caught its rays, and began to sparkle and scintillate with all the colours of the rainbow. Nocturnal animals ceased to prowl about, hastening to take refuge from the light in the darkness of dense shrubs, holes, and caves.

Quiet lay over the whole region, as if everything were astonished at the birth of day and spellbound by the rising sun.

All at once the pure morning air vibrated with the jubilant trill of a bird; it came so suddenly that the small baby archaic tapir trotting beside its mother on its way to breakfast in its favourite spot pressed close against the warm flank of its mother, quite forgetting its hunger for tasting more of those delicious green leaves it had filled itself with yesterday down there on the edge of the swamp. Then it heard another trill, and after a moment the whole region rang with the songs of birds. The feathered singers greeted one of the Tertiary mornings. Time had marched on in its inexorable and obstinate way, and had already long left behind the Mesozoic nights and days and animals. The reptiles had long since ceased to rule the world. A new time had arisen, and it had brought great changes with it. The Mesozoic world had given way the Tertiary world.

THE MAMMALS CONQUER THE WORLD

The Mesozoic ended with the fall of the reptiles; the *Middle Ages of the Animals* had come to an end. But the end of this era does not coincide with the end of the Middle Ages of the Plants, for that era finished in the Upper Cretaceous. Again we see how the animals depended upon the plants, and how the Mesozoic did not end until later than the Mesophytic.

A further major era in the evolution of the animals opened in the Tertiary. At its very beginning the rule of the reptiles had come to an end; all the important and striking saurian groups had become extinct at the end of the Mesozoic (we do not know all the causes of this); only a few poorly-represented reptilian groups (lizards, snakes, crocodiles, tortoises) continued into the Tertiary, occupying a very subordinate place in the Tertiary fauna. The leading place was taken by the *mammals*, and therefore the Tertiary is also known as the *Age of Mammals*.

Their richly-ramified development, especially that of the Placentalia, began as early as the very beginning of the Tertiary. It proceeded very rapidly, for in the Eocene the first Primates, Prosimians and Platyrrhinae, appeared, in the Oligocene the first Catarrhinae, the monkeys of the Old World and the ancestors of the first anthropoid apes made their appearance, and in the Miocene and Pliocene we already find the ancestors of the recent anthropoid apes, of orangutan, chimpanzee and gorilla. This surprising and explosive expansion of the mammals, diverging in all directions, was caused not only by the evolutionary youth of the mammal phylum, and thus also by its great adaptability to different living conditions, but also by the wealth of different environments which arose through great orogenetic activity (thus it was at that time that the uplifting of the Alps, the Carpathians, the Pyrenees, the Himalayas and other mountain systems ended, the activity of very many and very large volcanoes, the frequent inundations of the land by the sea, the splitting up of seas into smaller and less salty water basins, changes of climate and a sharper differentiation of the climatic zones, the transformation of swampy regions into dry steppes and the like. All this did not and could not fail to exert an influence on the evolution of the animals, especially of the mammals.

We must not forget either another favourable circumstance for the mammals. This was the unusual expansion of the flowering (covered-seed or angiosperm) plants, which certainly created exceptionally varied food for the fauna, and again particularly for the mammals. Many groups expanded successfully only because of the existence of flowering plants; others, for instance the monkeys, living mainly on fruit, pupae, and seeds, could originate and develop further only in the vicinity of flowering plants, while in the development of the birds and insects their role is still more obvious.

The oldest Tertiary mammals were very often mixed, collective types, that is, their skeletons show that they possessed the characteristics of two or more of the mammal groups of today; these collective types are very important, as they show us the path which the evolution of the different mammal groups and branches took, and these formed the starting point for yet others. Thus we know today with certainty that the Insectivora (insect-eaters) were the most primitive group of the higher mammals. We also know that some mammals returned to an aquatic environment, transformed their walking limbs into secondary swimming organs, and became exclusively aquatic mammals like the whales (Cetacea). The rich Tertiary mammal fauna, differentiated in shape, gave rise in the course of time also to many narrowly-specialised groups, which then in the further course of evolution could not adapt themselves sufficiently quickly and elastically to the changing conditions of their particular environment, and which were thus doomed to extinction (as *Uintatherium*, *Titanotherium*, *Arsinoitherium*, *Indricotherium*, *Deinotherium*, and many others). It is not possible in this survey to describe more precisely the early history of the evolution of many mammals, but it is sufficient to say that the history of the evolution of many mammals, as of the horses, proboscidia and beasts of prey, is known in great detail.

MAN ENTERS UPON THE SCENE

The Quaternary fauna is the evolutionary continuation of that in the Tertiary. As the Ice Age had a great influence on the evolution of plants, so it had also on the fauna. Among the latter there was also a migration of the thermophile types from south to north and of the cold-loving types from north to south, as interglacial and glacial periods alternated. As a typical animal of some glacial periods in Central Europe we may for instance mention the mammoth (*Mammonteus primigenius*), perhaps the best-known of all fossil animals, and its faithful companion, the woolly rhinoceros (*Coelodonta antiquitatis*).

In the evolution of living beings the Quaternary is, however, unusually important for the appearance of the first *primitive man*. Therefore the Quaternary is sometimes also called the *Anthropozoic*, i.e. the *Age of Man*.

It would be neither correct nor very consistent to assume that the general law of evolution does not apply to man. On the contrary, the origin of man in any other way than that of evolution is unthinkable from a biological point of view. Man also owes his existence to a long line of ancestors.

Charles Darwin voiced, and gave good grounds for accepting, the theory of the origin of man from animal forerunners, though in his time no evidence for this theory had as yet been found in the strata of the earth. Today we know many such proofs, and all of them confirm Darwin's view that man is a product of evolution. But it has to be emphasised—as Darwin himself did emphasise—that man does not derive from any of the monkeys or apes of today, but that he most probably shares a common ancestor with them, dating from the end of the Tertiary. Nowadays hardly anyone would be offended at the thought of the evolutionary origin of man. But it was a startlingly new idea when it was first put forward, and many people were grievously upset by it. But as that great contemporary of Charles Darwin, Thomas Huxley, said, thinking people who have freed themselves of antiquated superstitions will find in the lowly origin of man the best proof of his splendid potentialities, and in view of the constant progress of man in the past they can also find a reasonable basis for the faith that he has before him a great future.

EPILOGUE

We have finished our long pilgrimage through the depths of primeval time. And as we have carefully looked about us, we have become convinced that the world was not always as it is today, but that it has changed, that it has advanced from the simple to the more complex, until finally it has reached man himself. We have become convinced that evolution accompanies life from its very beginnings, and that it was evolution which gave branches to the tree of life, giving it width as well as height. We already know a number of the laws governing this evolution. In our pilgrimage we have noted particularly the influence of the environment on the living beings and all the consequences resulting from it. This law of evolution has been, because of its basic and universal validity, the one best suited for our explanation.

Even in Darwin's time many scientists declared that only paleontology could supply the main evidence for the correctness of the theory of the evolution of living beings. Today we may say that in this respect paleontology has not failed, and that it is largely due to the work done in paleontology that the theory of evolution has stood up to the tests of modern science. The latest discoveries, sometimes quite unexpected and surprising ones, have always fitted accurately into the place prepared for them by theory. Thus Professor Marcellin Boule and Professor Jean Piveteau rightly say that 'notwithstanding the contradictions and insufficiencies of many of its hypotheses paleontology has arranged an unshakable total of facts which show us that life possesses a history, that there are physical links between all beings, extinct and living, that the present is a function of the past. Thanks to it there is more unity, more order, more solidity and harmony in our understanding of the organic world, of what we today call the biosphere. Paleontology has improved our way of thinking by establishing in such an accurate manner the idea of the evolution of life'.

It is natural that we do not know the evolutionary prehistory of organisms in all the detail we should like. But we shall get to know it, for the untiring work, the knowledge, experience, persistence and love of the paleontologists for their mission yield every year many new discoveries and much knowledge. Even though it will take a long time, yet there will come a moment when the paleontologists will write footnotes to all the pages of the great chronicle of life, and make a full stop after the last word of the last chapter. We of today must be satisfied with the incomplete chronicle, but even this is sufficient for us to contemplate what has been with admiration and respect and to look forward with confidence and courage to what will be in the future.

PLATES

THE CAMBRIAN SEA

The traces left by the life which appeared on our Earth towards the end of the Archeozoic (about 1500 million years ago), cannot be detected for certain until the Proterozoic; they consist of rare and sporadic remains of algae, worms, primitive brachiopods, molluscs, and perhaps also crustaceans. The first expansion of life, which in trying to form a purposive unity with the environment constantly changed and constantly formed higher and higher evolutionary types, cannot be well observed until the very beginning of the Paleozoic, i.e. in the Cambrian. At that time life was already considerably advanced and differentiated.

The most characteristic representatives of the Cambrian fauna were the trilobites, which show a resemblance to the crustaceans. Their carapace was divided lengthwise into three parts—hence their name. The mouth opening was on the underside of the head; on the upper side there was often a pair of compound eyes. The flat shape of the body and the position of the mouth indicate that the trilobites mostly crawled on the sea bottom, where they collected and ate minute organisms or organic débris. Various kinds of primitive brachiopods, echinoderms (especially the extinct Cystoidea), worms, Hydrozoa, and sponges lived at the same time as the trilobites in these earliest seas.

Some 570 million years ago the Cambrian sea covered part of Central Europe. In the sediments of this sea we find today the remains of the oldest fauna. The picture shows part of the bottom of the Cambrian sea in Central Bohemia with the characteristic trilobites of the species *Paradoxides gracilis* (large, spiny) and *Ellipsocephalus hoffi* (small), together with siliceous sponges and medusas swimming above a growth of various algae.

PL. 1

THE SILURIAN SEA

In the Silurian age, some 400 million years before our time, life was already rich and manifold, and from the evolutionary viewpoint it had advanced considerably beyond life in the earlier (Cambrian and Ordovician) seas. In addition to trilobites and the strange graptolites the primitive representatives of the gastropods, lamellibranchs, brachiopods and bryozoa attained wide distribution. Of the echinoderms the crinoids were most notable; their long stems carried at the end an ornamental cup with a wreath of five movable arms. Also the precursors of our present corals spread considerably in these seas, and formed in suitable places extensive and picturesque growths. Numerous primitive cephalopods formed an important element of the fauna of the Silurian seas; all the cephalopods were related to the modern *Nautilus*, but they usually had a straight or only slightly bent shell, often decorated with beautiful coloured patterns.

Our picture shows a rocky part of the Silurian sea of Central Bohemia, where among the mats of various algae and the beautiful crinoid species *Scyphocrinites excavatus*, we find loaf-shaped clumps of the extinct corals of the Tabulata genus *Favosites*, and the solitary calyces of the extinct corals of the Tetracoralla genera *Xylodes* (high, narrow calyces) and *Omphyma* (low, cup-shaped calyces). On the sand in front of the rock trilobites of the species *Aulacopleura konincki* and *Cheirurus insignis* (spiny) crawl about, and carnivorous cephalopods of the species *Orthoceras pellucidum* (with a straight shell) and *Cyrtoceras decurio* (with a slightly bent shell) lie in ambush. Empty gastropod shells (helically coiled shell of the genus *Murchisonia* and plano-spirally coiled shell of the genus *Cyclotropis*) are half embedded in the sand. In the right corner of the picture is a small group of brachiopods of the species *Glasia columbella* (smooth shells) and *Conchidium knighti* (shells decorated with costae).

(The picture was reconstructed from the fauna of the Budňany Beds from the sites at Kosoř and at Velká Chuchle, near Prague. The coloured patterns on the shells of the cephalopods were painted from remains deposited in the National Museum in Prague.)

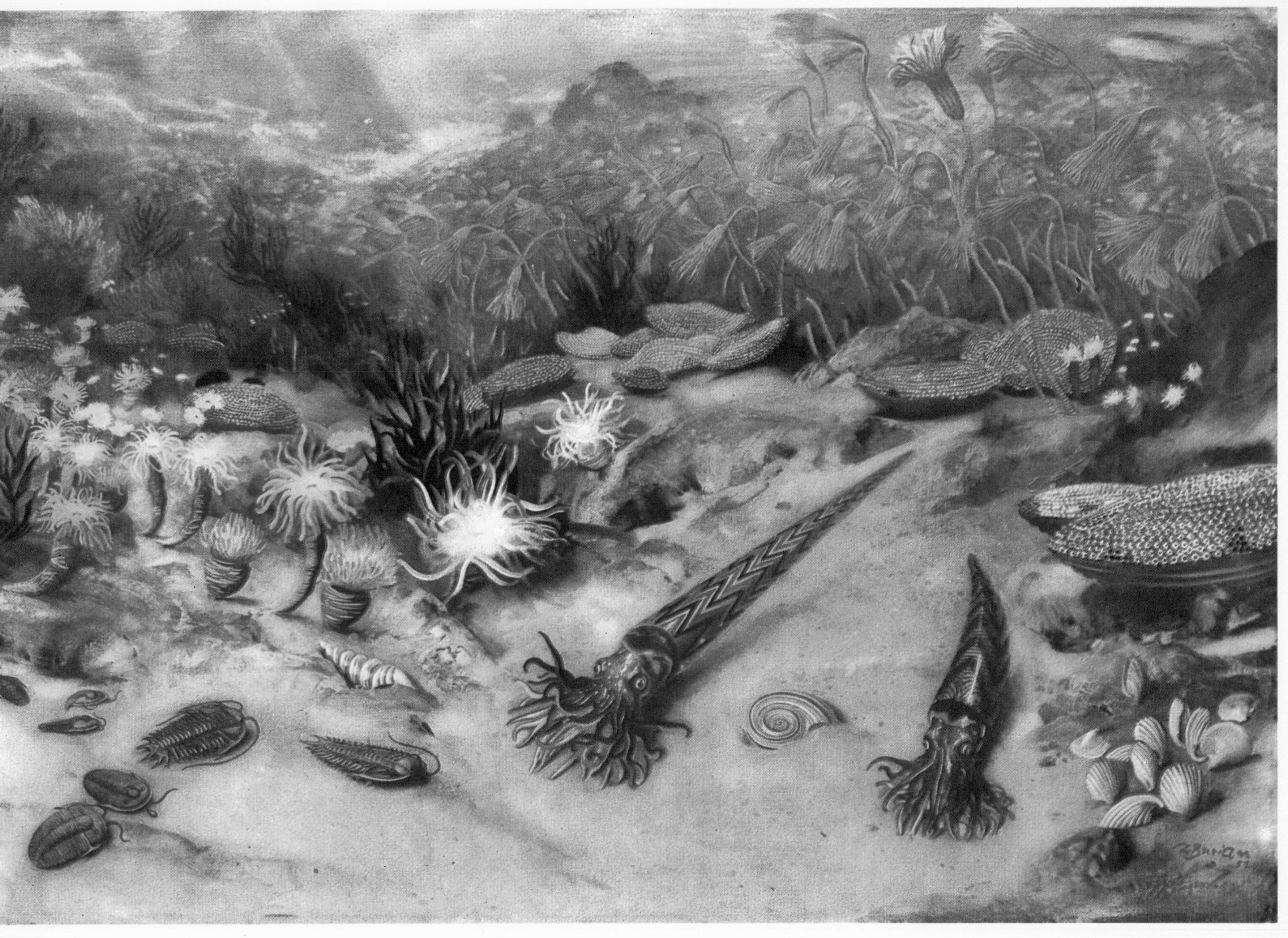

PL. 2

PTERYGOTUS AND EURYPTERUS

The spider-like arthropods (Arachnomorpha) flourished greatly in the Silurian seas, especially those of the group of the Merostomata. They were strange animals whose body was composed of a relatively small cephalothorax and a long abdomen of twelve segments. Behind the last segment there was as a rule a separate, usually spiny caudal appendage, the telson. The cephalothorax carried on its underside six pairs of appendages, partly oral, partly serving for walking. On the upper side of the cephalothorax, in addition to the large compound eyes there were still separate small eyes, the so-called ocelli.

Two genera of these peculiar animals were especially prominent in the Silurian seas, namely *Eurypterus* and *Pterygotus*. The former genus (*Eurypterus*) is relatively small, and is particularly interesting, as the last (sixth) pair of appendages is transformed into large rowing organs; the latter genus (*Pterygotus*), sometimes up to about six feet long, is characterised by the second pair of appendages terminating in large claws, not unlike the claws of lobsters or crabs, and by the surface of its chitinous carapace being covered with very characteristic crescent-shaped ornamentations. Both these genera were abundantly distributed in the Silurian seas.

They were all beasts of prey. Some of them, as for instance the huge *Pterygotus* or the still larger *Stylonurus* (over ten feet) had no serious rivals among the fauna of that time. It seems that one of them (*Carcinosoma*), reminiscent of a large scorpion, vanquished its prey by jabbing it with its pointed and bent sword-like telson, which was presumably provided with a poison gland.

PL. 3

DINICHTHYS AND CLADOSELACHE

The waters of the Devonian period will for ever remain memorable for the great expansion of the fishes. Among them the representatives of the group called Placoderms belong to the oldest and most primitive early fishes. They have been known for a long time, and were discovered by the Scottish quarryman Hugh Miller. Their endoskeleton was more or less ossified, their exoskeleton was composed of ossified, very strong and sometimes also large plates. We can divide them roughly into two groups according to whether their pointed pectoral fins are composed of one segment (Arthrodira) or of several segments (Antiarcha). The earliest fishes of the former group (Arthrodira), characterised by large heads covered with a great number of regularly-arranged bony plates and mostly enclosed together with the anterior part of the body in a bony armature, lived in lagoons with brackish water; we know them from the Devonian of Europe, North America, and Australia. *Dinichthys*, with a head-shield more than three feet long, was one of the giants of these earliest fishes. Its prey often included the ancient shark (Proselachia), especially the primitive genus *Cladoselache*, whose fusiform body, about 2 ft. 4 in. long, had large triangular pleural fins and a strong tail fin. Their vertebral column was not yet segmented and only the vertebral arches were well developed and ossified. The paired fins had a short cartilaginous base from which the fin rays ran out.

More than 350 million years have passed since the earliest fishes of the genus *Dinichthys* hunted not only the earliest sharks of the genus *Cladoselache* but also many other fishes, lung fishes Crossopterygii, which in a great abundance of genera and species, lived together with them. The Devonian waters, in which the origin and first expansion of many groups of fishes took place, have long vanished from the surface of the Earth. But their mud, today solidified into stone, has preserved remains of the bodies of these strange fishes and still proclaims that from an evolutionary point of view the Devonian is the age of the fishes.

PL. 4

THE LOWER DEVONIAN LANDSCAPE

It was towards the end of the Lower Paleozoic, towards the end of the Silurian and at the beginning of the Devonian, some 370 million years ago, that a memorable event took place on our Earth, for it was at that time that some types of plants tried to leave the waters of the extinct seas and to occupy first swampy coastal soil and later also the dry soil farther inland. This was astonishing because the dry land was at that time still desert, entirely without life. Only the naked rocks, whipped by downpours and winds, rose darkly over the endless plains. After heavy storms the shores of the then seas were bordered by narrow strips of thrown-up algae, among which glittered the coloured shells of gastropods, lamellibranchs, and cephalopods, and where the articulated bodies of trilobites lay without motion. But even these strips disappeared in time, and the desolation of the landscape reappeared in all its terrifying monotony.

The plants had to attack the dry land many times before they finally conquered it. Many of their attempts failed, but finally the plants were victorious, and a new home of infinite possibilities was gained. Thus it came about that as early as the Lower Devonian a strange flora had taken possession of the coastal swamps and marshes, and its low and shy whispering was the first sound to be heard on dry land, which until then had been barren and dead. This Lower Devonian flora had no conspicuous shapes and sizes. There were here the most primitive and fundamental types of vascular cryptogams belonging to the long extinct group of the Psilophytales. Their axes grew from bulbous or creeping rootstocks, branched furcately, and carried spore vessels at their tops. They were leafless (e.g. the herb genera *Rhynia* and *Horneophyton*) or leafy (e.g. *Psilophyton*). Some of their types also grew from the mud of the shallow coastal waters (*Taeniocrada*, *Zosterophyllum*). But notwithstanding their simplicity and modest appearance these earliest Lower Devonian growths were of great evolutionary importance, as the history of the land flora begins with them.

PL. 5

THE MIDDLE DEVONIAN LANDSCAPE

We already know that it was towards the end of the Silurian and at the beginning of the Devonian that the plants, like serried ranks of waves turned into foam, threw themselves in rhythmic surges on the muddy or sandy shores, there to attack unceasingly the dry land in order to conquer it. They disregarded the dead with which they strewed their pioneer road, they disregarded obstacles and setbacks, and obstinately hurried forward, changing and adapting themselves until finally (as we also already know), in the Lower Devonian they were victorious. The grandeur of this victory does not, however, show at all in the simplicity and plainness of the Lower Devonian land flora. This consisted only of the small, modest and shy precursors of the later tree-like horse-tails, lycopods and ferns, which grew in picturesque groups on constantly larger and larger areas of the continents, relieving the monotonous greyish-yellow solitude with bright spots of green of the most varied shades.

In the Middle Devonian land flora the representatives of the group of the Psilophytales retreated into the background, though many specimens of it were still common (as the leafless tree-like *Pseudosporochnus*, the leafy and creeping *Drepanophycus*, or *Asteroxylon*, up to 3 ft. 6 in. high, presumably growing from the mud of shallow waters). Though all became extinct towards the end of the Middle Devonian, before their dying out there developed from some of their types the first lycopods (*Protolepidodendron*, *Barrandeina*, *Duisbergia*, up to seven feet high, and *Archaeosigillaria*, the first really tree-like type), horse-tails (*Hyenia* and *Calamophyton*), and ferns (especially *Protopteridium*).

Compared with the Lower Devonian vegetation the flora of the Middle Devonian was much richer and much more diversified. It received its main character from the different types of horse-tails, lycopods and ferns, which already formed picturesque groves and small woods bordering the banks of the pools and swamps. But evolution advanced constantly. Thus the end of the Devonian offers an entirely different picture of the flora from that at its beginning. In the Upper Devonian, when the flora was enriched still further by the first tree-like horse-tails (*Pseudobornia*) and by further tree-like types of lycopods (*Cyclostigma*) and ferns, there appeared on our Earth the first true primeval forests as far as both appearance and size are concerned.

PL. 6

THE PRIMEVAL CARBONIFEROUS FOREST

In the large well-watered basins at the foot of the mountains raised by the great orogenetic process of the Hercynian folding towards the end of the Devonian and at the beginning of the Carboniferous, a luxuriant vegetation grew up under exceptionally favourable living conditions, and the débris of this flora became the basis of the present deposits of black coal, a raw material which man is only today beginning to appreciate as it deserves.

Vascular cryptogams were among the most characteristic types of the primeval forests of the Carboniferous period, especially the tree-like lycopods (*Lepidodendron* with a richly-branched crown, and *Sigillaria* with one or more tufts of long narrow leaves) and horse-tails (*Eucalamites*, *Stylocalamites*, and *Calamitina* with large, articulated trunks with whorls of branches studded with whorls of straight leaves). Below these tree-like giants, 72 to 110 ft. high, spread a luxuriant undergrowth of mosses, hepaticae, herbaceous and creeping lycopods, and magnificent ferns. But there also grew here ferns which wound themselves like lianas round the trunks of lepidodendrons, sigillariae and others (e.g. *Mariopteris* or *Etapteris*) or which as trees, 36 to 54 ft. high, formed delightful groves. The strange stenophylla (*Sphenophyllum*) wound themselves around the stumps of fallen plant giants or on the trunks of tree-like ferns. The remarkable representatives of the extinct group of the Pteridospermae had their home among these cryptogams, and though in appearance very similar to the ferns, they none the less formed true seeds (as e.g. *Neuropteris*, *Lyginopteris* and others). All the representatives of the group of the Pteridospermae belong to the lowest of the Gymnospermae. Though the abundant Pteridospermae were of relatively low growth, they had unusually large leaf-fans. The tallest trees in the primeval forests of the Carboniferous were the *Cordaites*, also belonging to the Gymnosperms; they were up to 145 ft. high and had a smooth trunk and a richly branched crown with long, ribbon-like leaves; several species grew here.

This is in rough outline what the primeval forests of the Carboniferous looked like, the splendid green adornment of the landscapes some 300 million years ago. Today they are buried deep in the earth in the form of coal seams. When you poke your fire, remember that you have before your eyes, not some valueless black lumps of stone unworthy of attention but a true monument of the primeval forest of the Carboniferous period.

PL. 7

PLEURACANTHUS AND AMBLYPTERUS

The rivers and pools of the primeval forests of the Carboniferous were also rich in life. In the mud on their bottom lived various worms and lamellibranchs, on the stalks crawled, though only rarely, gastropods, which conquered the dry land for the first time about now; among the tangled vegetation darted the larvae of manifold insects. Various small crustaceans were also abundant.

The earliest sharks of the genus *Pleuracanthus* were the large beasts of prey of these waters. They had a cartilaginous endoskeleton, but crowded with irregular calcareous prisms. The upper and lower vertebral arches were ossified and had long spines. The skull was cartilaginous. There were five gill arches, and according to some paleontologists they were even covered by a kind of gill lid. The dorsal fin was long; it began behind the skull and extended to the tail. The pectoral fins had an articulated median axis with rays on both sides; the males had the copulation organ in the pelvic fin. A strong spine with teeth-like points on both sides jutted out behind the head anterior to the dorsal fin. The tail fin was asymmetrical. The mouth was armed with a great number of teeth, with two divergent points, between which there remained a small median point. These sharks were very abundant in the waters of the Carboniferous forests of Czechoslovakia, and attained a length of about 28 inches. The Czech paleontologist Professor A. Frič contributed much to their investigation by studying their remains from the Upper Carboniferous of Nýřany and from the Lower Permian of Broumov.

These sharks certainly took a heavy toll of the shoals of fish of that time, especially of certain types of the extinct families Palaeoniscidae and Platysomidae. These were mostly smallish fishes having a slender flattened body with large rhombic scales and a mouth armed with small teeth. These fishes were also abundant in the Carboniferous swamps of Czechoslovakia, in the Upper Carboniferous as well as in the Lower Permian; the most numerous of them was the genus *Amblypterus*, with many species.

PL. 8

MEGANEURA

From the rosy cradle of the morning sky the burning sun of the Upper Carboniferous sent forth its rays. Before its golden arrows the clouds of mists retreated into the densest parts of the strange, ancient vegetation, which grew luxuriantly everywhere.

It was a strange landscape which now appeared in the light of breaking dawn.

It consisted of innumerable islands, separated by a maze of straits and channels, a chaotic medley of shallow lakes, swamps and dry soil. Stiff clumps of huge calamites grew from the muddy bottom of the coastal waters; the slender, scarred trunks of lepidodendrons raised their huge, umbrella-like, expanded crowns high above the moist soil of the shores, while the related sigillaria lifted columnar trunks, likewise covered with scars left by fallen leaves, terminated by tufts of long sword-shaped foliage. Here and there grew also magnificent tree-ferns, sometimes also a slender cordaites remarkable for its dark green leaves. On the trunks of some of these gigantic trees various liana-like ferns climbed upwards like large green snakes, their large leaf-fans swayed to and fro in the moist air like beautiful banners of green lace, and wherever the wild gales had broken and overturned the titanic trees, the moist soil was covered with an impenetrable network of low vegetation and thickets of young calamites, lepidodendrons and sigillaria.

An almost terrifying silence brooded over this swampy landscape.

But this silence did not mean that it was devoid of life. Among the dense clumps of low ferns the earliest scorpions and spiders lay in ambush, waiting for their prey. Numerous myriapods hid under the rotting plant remains. The earliest insects (especially of the group Palaeodictyoptera) were also richly represented; their bodies still bore a number of ancient, primitive features, and they became the basis for the evolution of a more modern, higher type, already represented here by some forms such as large cockroaches, the strange forerunners of grasshoppers, ephemerae and others. Some of the earliest insects and some true insect types attained a considerable size. The dragonfly *Meganeura*, with a wing-span of up to 30 inches, was a real insect giant.

PL. 9

THE STEGOCEPHALIANS

The virgin forests of the Carboniferous period with their innumerable swamps were the home also of the earliest amphibia, the stegocephalians, which had developed during the Devonian from the Crossopterigii. They lived in the forests in countless genera and species, and are so important for the Upper Carboniferous and Lower Permian that these two geological periods are called the Age of the Amphibia. This name is most apposite, not only because the amphibia were then numerically strong, but also because they realy dominated the whole world. These amphibia were of different sizes and shapes; some were like salamanders of lizards, others like crocodiles or snakes. Their bodies were covered with an armour consisting of fine scales or rods; in some large forms this armour consisted of heavy, strong bony plates. The heads of the stegocephalians were flat, mostly of triangular shape, and their mouths were armed with sharp teeth, showing that they were beasts of prey; sometimes they did not spare even their own young ones. They are distinguished from recent amphibia by the invariably greater number of cranial bones which completely enclosed the skull and covered it over (hence the name stegocephalian), the *foramen parietale,* the characteristic structure of the shoulder girdle, the labyrinthodontic teeth, and the remarkable development of the body armour. The adult stegocephalians lived especially on the moist banks of the swamps, lakes and pools, where among the profusion of the ancient flora they prowled round in search of worms, myriapods, cockroaches, and other small prey; the large stegocephalians were presumably mainly hunters of fish. They laid their eggs in the water, where larvae breathing with external gills hatched from them.

These interesting primitive amphibia lived in great numbers in the Carboniferous and Lower Permian swamps. Our picture shows a quiet nook of the Upper Carboniferous swamp at Nýřany in Bohemia. A dark *Branchiosaurus salamandroides* rests on a flat stone; below it lies *Microbrachis pelikani*, characterised by small limbs. One *Urocordylus scalaris* darts up after some insect onto the stone in the middle of the water, while a second one observes with curiosity how a serpent-like *Dolichosoma longissimum* comes suddenly into view, apparently from nowhere.

PL. 10

EDAPHOSAURUS

The surface of the Upper Carboniferous swamp sparkled in the golden sunlight. From the swampy shores virgin forests of giant lepidodendrons mirrored themselves in the water as in a sheet of silver. The reflection of these ancient tree-like lycopods was interrupted only in the places where clumps of calamites had grown up from the shallow coastal waters of the swamps; their big, articulated and tall trunks with numerous whorls of branches and slender leaves were firmly anchored in the thin mud by strong roots running in all directions. Low ferns, mosses and hepaticae threw their green veil over every deep and moist fissure in the rocks. Tree-ferns, whose large leaf-fans grew only on the sides of the trunk, enhanced the fairy-like beauty of this ancient landscape.

Below a high dark rock a strange large saurian, *Edaphosaurus*, rested, while another one of the same genus and species stood opposite on a big boulder. They were strange animals, whose fantastic appearance made them fit well into the ancient landscape. Their most characteristic feature was the enormous comb-like frill of long bony spines with tubercles which ran along their back; these spines were nothing but the lengthened upper appendages of the vertebrae. Though they looked terrifying, they were innocent herbivores, as indeed their teeth betray. These queer saurians lived in the Upper Carboniferous and Lower Permian in Europe and North America. In Czechoslovakia their remains have been found in two localities, at Nýřany in Bohemia and at Rosice in Moravia, both of them Upper Carboniferous sites. We may, however, assume that these saurians also lived in Moravia in the Lower Permian. This is indicated by the discovery of large footprints, which were found long ago in the sandstones of the Lower Permian at Ivančice, near Rosice. Of course this is only a theory, for these footprints may belong to some large stegocephalian.

PL. 11

MOSCHOPS

A large part of South Africa is covered with layers known technically in geological and paleontological literature as the Karroo formation. This complex of beds is composed of alternating varicoloured shales, marls and sandstones of continental origin, and is about 18,000 ft. thick; it was deposited from the end of the Paleozoic (i.e. from the Permian) through the whole early Mesozoic (until the Jurassic). Continental sediments of the same geological age occur, however, elsewhere in the southern hemisphere, especially in South America, in Australia, and in India. These occurrences represent today all that remains of a former more extensive and continous southern continetnt, called Gondwana.

This southern Permotriassic Gondwana land was (in addition to many other regions, especially the Permian sub-Uralian region) the home of strange archaic reptiles, sometimes characterised by an interesting mixture of the features of archaic amphibia (stegocephalians), reptiles and mammals. These early reptiles formed a large and varied complex, which is just as interesting as for instance the later groups of Jurassic or Cretaceous reptiles or of Tertiary mammals. They were of different size, appearance and habits. From an evolutionary point of view they are of outstanding importance, as it was among them that the types (the group Ictidosauria) occurred from which the first mammals developed.

Many very ponderous and clumsy archaic reptiles lived in the Permian of South Africa, and they formed a number of separate evolutionary branches with dead ends. One of these clumsy beasts was *Moschops*, more than 7 ft. long, which in the Middle Permian shared the banks of desert rivers with a sparse vegetation, which it used as food.

PL. 12

MESOSAURUS

As the Permian continent of the southern hemisphere had its entirely characteristic and interesting reptile complex, so had the waters of the southern hemisphere their peculiar and strange saurian, *Mesosaurus*. It was not very big, only about 28 inches long. Its skull was elongated, and its jaws were endowed with a great number of fine but sharp teeth of different sizes, growing in alveoli. Its neck was short but the body was elongated and ended in a long tail. The dorsal ribs were strikingly thickened; thischaracteristic (called pachyostosis) was a feature of adaptation to an aquatic life, and is reminiscent of a similar phenomenon observed in recent and fossil Sirenians. The hind-limbs were much stronger than the fore-limbs, and their digits were considerably lengthened. The fore- and the hind-limbs had five digits.

Remains of this saurian are known so far only from the Permian of South Africa and Brazil. It is extremely interesting, as it is the oldest aquatic reptile; the reptiles developed first as land animals, which only later took to a life in water.

Formerly this small carnivorous saurian was regarded as the ancestor of the ichthyosauri. Today, however, we know from the detailed investigations of Professor F. von Huene that this is not the case.

PL. 13

THE MESOZOIC LANDSCAPE

When the Lower Permian ended, and the virgin Carboniferous forest, full of primeval beauty, disappeared for ever from the surface of our Earth, the Upper Permian set in, and a striking change took place in the plant world. Instead of vast jungles of cryptogamous plants, many of which attained a tree-like growth of often surprising size, gymnosperms (as *Ullmannia*, *Baiera*, *Voltzia*), appeared abundantly, only, however, as harbingers of their later great expansion and flourishing, which lasted through almost the whole of the Mesozoic (till the end of the Lower Cretaceous). Thus the vegetation (of course only on rough, general lines) made the Mesozoic scene look different from the Permian scene.

The leading types of the Mesozoic flora were various gymnosperms, principal among them various representatives of the cycadophytes, low forms with short, globular or barrel-shaped trunks (Cycadoidea) covered sometimes with large flowers of different colours, and tree-like forms with slender, only occasionally branching stems, but both with a rich crown of long and tough leaves, resembling palms. The representatives of the extinct group of the Bennettitaceae of shrub-like (*Wielandiella* or *Williamsoniella*) or tree-like shape (e.g. *Williamsonia*) belong also to the cycadophytes. Representatives of the conifers appeared, too, and spread abundantly; they consisted of various members of the Ginkgoales (also the genus *Ginkgo* itself), taxodiums, trees of a pine-like and cypress-like character, and others. It was also at that time that the huge sequoia appeared for the first time.

The cryptogams lost in the Mesozoic age their former leading position among the vegetation. Various ferns (*Thaumatopteris*, *Dipteridium*, *Hausmannia*, etc.) still grew in shady and damp places or on the banks of some river or lake, sometimes also creeping over moist rocks (e.g. *Gleichenia*). Various horse-tails grew from the waters of the pools (*Equisetum*, *Schizoneura*), but they were far smaller than before, and their distribution was much less wide.

The Mesozoic vegetation was thus different from that of the preceding age, with the result that the fauna too was different; it lived in regions of a different nature, and it utilised vigorously for its further evolution and expansion what this more bountiful Mesozoic world had to offer.

PL. 14

MASTODONSAURUS

The stegocephalians, of which so many genera and species lived in the waters and moist places of the swampy virgin forests in the Upper Carboniferous and Lower Permian, became completely extinct at the beginning of the Mesozoic era (in the Triassic). But their last representatives in the Triassic are interesting because they attained a considerable, indeed an amazing size. The largest of them was *Mastodonsaurus*. The skull alone of the species *Mastodonsaurus giganteus*, which lived in the German Upper Triassic, was three and a half feet long; this is a size which to this day has not been surpassed by any living or extinct amphibian.

In their general appearance the Mastodonsauri resembled huge frogs; they were feared as beasts of prey, living mainly on fishes whose remains have been found in their fossilised faeces. At Bedheim in Thuringia a skull of the species *Mastodonsaurus acuminatus* was discovered, and in its mouth was found a tooth of a dipnoan fish of the genus *Ceratodes* and six small teeth of a fish of the genus *Saurichthyes*, which thus confirms the fact that fishes were the principal food of these large and carnivorous amphibians.

The mastodonsauri seem to have been exclusively aquatic animals, which only occasionally left the water; but they never stayed long on dry land, and returned as soon as possible to their true environment.

We find their skeletal remains in great numbers in many localities. The main reason for this is that the large lakes or swamps in which the mastodonsauri lived constantly shrank through evaporation, until finally there remained only small pools full of the huge amphibians, which had retreated to them from all sides as the waters receded. When the last drop of water disappeared from these pools, the dead bodies of the mastodonsauri lay on the muddy bottom, unable to live without water.

At least 200 million years have passed since these strange amphibians lived and became extinct, the last huge descendants of the Upper Carboniferous and Lower Permian stegocephalians.

PL. 15

CHIROTHERIUM

In the Lower Triassic, large sandy wastes covered the ground somewhere in present Germany. Only where shallow lakes formed in depressions there grew a sparse, xerophytic flora, especially the coniferous *Voltzia*, low cycads, and here and there tufts of low ferns (*Neuropteridium*, *Anomopteris*), whose leaf-fans were composed of tough leaflets standing close side by side. The slopes of the dunes were anchored by groups of the strange *Pleuromeia*, up to seven feet high, related to the Carboniferous Sigillaria; its slender trunks, with scars left by fallen-off leaves, were crowned by short coarse leaves and terminated in cones. Only the horse-tail *Schizoneura* grew from the shallow water at the shores of the lakes; but even here it had to struggle for existence when the burning rays of the Lower Triassic sun dried out the lakes, and their coastal shallows often turned into swampy land. More than once the mysterious saurian *Chirotherium* waddled on to the boggy ground and imprinted indelible footprints, preserved for ages.

Though the footprints of Chirotherium have long been known (from England since 1824, from Germany since 1835, from France since 1856, and from Spain since 1898), not even the smallest bone of this saurian has been found. Their five-digited footprints, like the imprints of a hand (hence their name), were for long a controversial subject among paleontologists. Some saw in them the footprints of mammals (for instance apes), others of amphibians, still others of reptiles, which indeed proved correct. The German paleontologist W. Soergel deserves great honour for this recognition of the reptilian origin of these footprints; after careful investigation he arrived at the conclusion that the Chirotherium was a saurian from the extinct group Pseudosuchia, which he also roughly reconstructed. The paleontologists did not surrender even when faced with the mystery of the Chirotherium, but on the contrary, with the tenacity proper to them, they used all their knowledge and experience in order to determine just from the footprints which animal had made them and how it looked. It would be a great victory for the human intellect should the find of a real skeleton confirm all the conclusions which the paleontologists have drawn on the mere basis of footprints.

PL. 16

STENOPTERYGIUS

The ichthyosaurids, or fish-lizards, are among the most abundant carnivorous saurians of the Mesozoic seas. They are suitably named, as the shape of their bodies was really fish-like. Their skin was bare. The skull was elongated, and the mouth was generally armed with numerous large and sharp teeth, sometimes up to as many as 200. We also know ichthyosaurids, however, which had in their mouths smaller, weaker and less numerous teeth, or else were completely toothless, like those which lived mainly on various cephalopods, especially cuttle-fish; those which lived on fish always had well-developed teeth. The limbs were transformed into fin-like organs. The strong, fish-shaped body was terminated by a large, leathery and vertically placed fin. In the geologically younger types this was crescent-shaped, with a larger inferior lobe, whose support was formed by the end of the vertebral column.

The average size of the ichthyosaurids was about 7 ft. We have knowledge also of species which attained considerable lengths. The largest giant was *Leptopterygius acutirostris* of the Lower Jurassic of Europe; the skull of this monster measured more than 7 ft., which corresponds to a total length of about 43 ft.

Not only remains of the last meal consumed by the ichthyosaurids have been found in their body cavities but also remains of their young ones, partly in embryo and partly devoured. The ichthyosaurids were viviparous. The embryo was born with the tail first, and its arrival in the world was not sudden, but took place over a period of weeks. The tail of the full-grown embryo protruded more and more from the female and only when, in this state, the embryo had learned to use its fins, especially its tail-fin, did it permanently leave the body of the mother. A premature and sudden birth would have been very dangerous for the helpless young one. Thus there is here a certain analogy to the birth of the young in the modern dolphin sturgeon which inhabits the Arctic *Delphinapterus leucas.* Such a manner of birthwas discovered in a beautifully preservedskeleton of a female of the species *Stenopterygius quadriscissus* from the Lower Jurassic of Germany. (This species is depicted on our plate.)

Many injuries have been discovered on the skeletons of these ichthyosaurids; they are mainly broken ribs, where, however, the bone has knitted well again. They need not all be injuries from battles with other carnivorous saurians, as for instance the plesiosaurids, but may be the result of fighting over females.

PL. 17

EURHINOSAURUS

Many different genera and species of ichthyosaurids lived in the Mesozoic seas. One of the most interesting was *Eurhinosaurus longirostris*, which inhabited the Lower Jurassic sea of South Germany. It is noteworthy for the unequal length of its toothed jaws. We do not really know why this was so.

In the Mesozoic the ichthyosaurids were distributed over all the existing seas, but towards the end of the age they became extinct. Their bones and skeletons are found almost throughout the world. The most beautifully and completely preserved skeletons are, however, found in the dark Jurassic shales at the foot of the Swabian Alps. Probably every major museum has, in its paleontological collections, some ichthyosaurid from this region. Like pressed flowers in a herbarium, so the skeletons of these carnivorous marine saurians lie in the dark shales. But we should be making a great mistake if we imagined that they were found in the quarries in the state in which we now see them with admiration and wonder in the museum. By then they are the result of masterly preparation, mostly by Dr. h. c. Bernhard Hauff of Holzmaden. The expert 'preparer' attacks the saurian with chisel and hammer, frees it more and more from the stone cover, extracts it bit by bit from its rocky tomb. In doing so he has, however, to see 'through the stone' in order not to remove a bone by mistake. This of course demands long practice, great patience, and naturally a certain knowledge of the skeleton of the saurian. This coarser preparation is followed by a finer one; with many burins, knives and needles of the most varied shapes and sizes, the preparer uncovers bone after bone, tooth after tooth. The time taken by such preparation-work depends on the size of the ichthyosaurid; it is reckoned that a skilled operator, working intensively and diligently, needs about three months to prepare an ichthyosaurus 9 ft. long. In the case of a specimen with the skin preserved the preparation takes much longer. Beautifully-prepared skeletons of ichthyosaurids are expensive. Before World War II a prepared skeleton of an ichthyosaurus about 7 ft. long cost about £ 750, with the skin preserved at least twice as much.

Although the ichthyosaurids closely approach the fishes or dolphins in appearance, there is no affinity between them. Their considerable outer resemblance is only the symptom of a very perfect adaptation to life in water.

PL. 18

CRYPTOCLEIDUS

The plesiosaurids were also characteristic carnivorous saurians of the Mesozoic seas. They were weird-looking reptiles with a short body, flattened underneath, and a short tail, but they had a very long neck, and a small head with a mouth full of sharp teeth. These saurians, too, had a bare skin, and their limbs were transformed into fin-like organs. They were feared as beasts of prey. They lay constantly in ambush, and woe to the creature which crossed their path. Fish were not quick enough to escape them, the shells of molluscs were not hard enough to resist their strong teeth. In the skeleton of a plesiosaurid from the Cretaceous, remains of the last food it consumed have been preserved in the body cavity; a close investigation of these remains showed that the plesiosaurid had last eaten carrion from a pterosaurid, a fish and a cephalopod, which it had greedily swallowed together with the crushed shell.

Besides these long-necked plesiosaurids we know also of short-necked ones; these always had a heavy, long skull, but otherwise the shape of the body was the same as the long-necked ones.

One of the most abundant and famous plesiosaurids was *Plesiosaurus*, well known from many complete skeletons, sometimes up to 18 ft. long, found in the Lower Jurassic of England and Germany. The beautifully-prepared skeletons of this saurian from the Jurassic of Holzmaden in Germany are also the masterly work of D. Hauff. In addition to this genus still other genera (as *Thaumatosaurus*, *Eretmosaurus*, *Cryptocleidus* and *Macrocleidus*) lived in the Mesozoic seas.

The plesiosaurids first appeared at the very outset of the Mesozoic, in the Triassic seas, but at that time there were only a few of them. They began to multiply in the Lower Jurassic seas, and in the Cretaceous they achieved world-wide distribution. With the end of the Cretaceous period they too disappeared, and the marine fauna was for ever deprived of these strange carnivorous saurians.

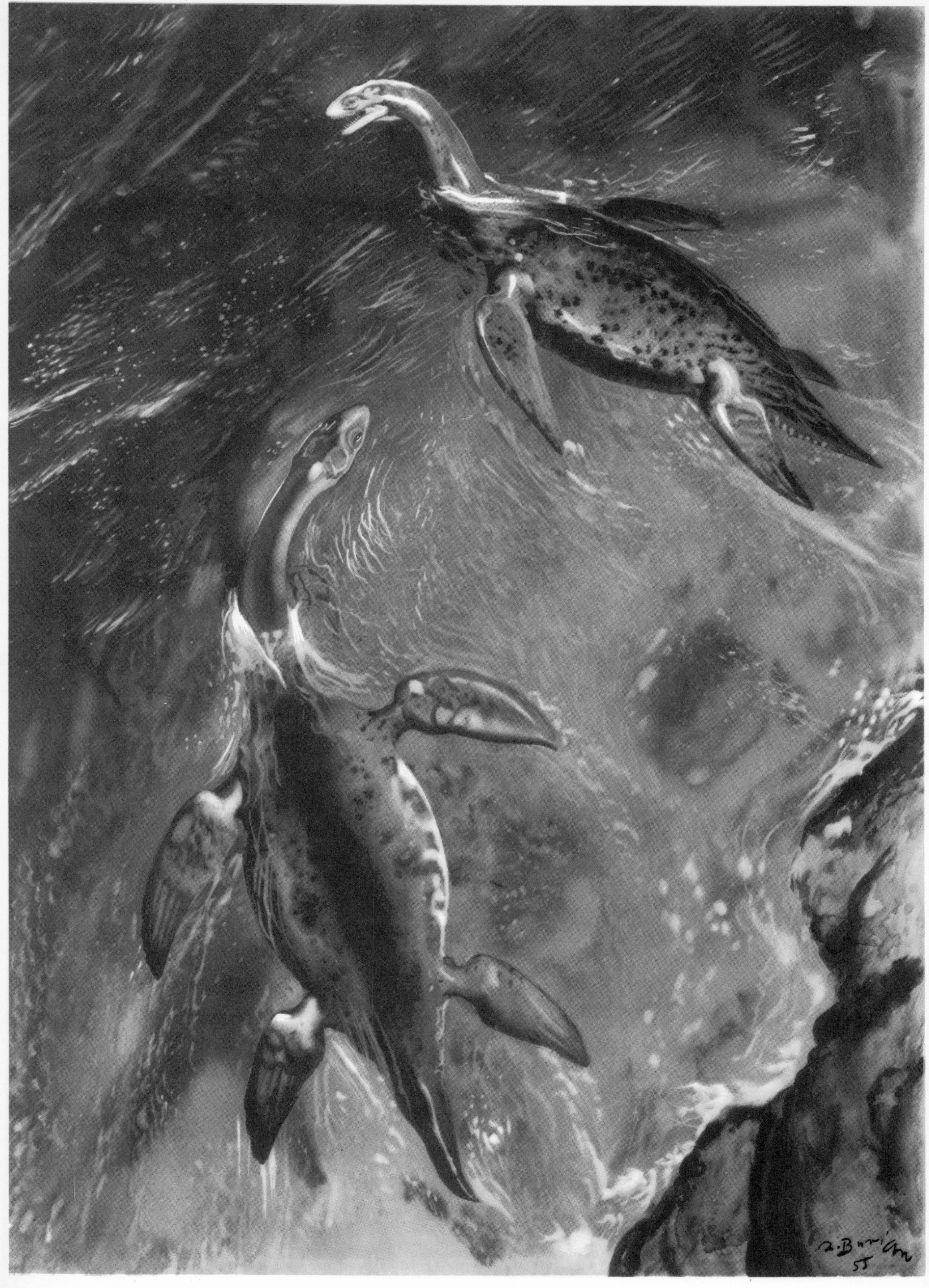

PL. 19

ELASMOSAURUS

The most remarkable long-necked plesiosaurid was the Upper Cretaceous *Elasmosaurus* from America. It attained a length of up to 47 ft. Of course a considerable part of this unusual size was due to the long neck composed of 76 vertebrae, a number not yet surpassed by any known extinct or living vertebrate.

Elasmosaurus lived in the Upper Cretaceous sea of Kansas, together with the huge Tylosaurus, which was no less ferocious. They certainly had bitter fights which flushed the huge pterosaurians, the pteranodons.

It is of interest that a miniature double of the American Elasmosaurus lived in the Lower Cretaceous sea of Germany; this was *Brancasaurus*, only 8 ft. long and with a neck of only 37 vertebrae.

The plesiosaurids have been known for a long time. Their first skeletons were scientifically recorded as early as 1824. But these finds and descriptions, listed in the paleontological literature as the oldest, are certainly not the first. This is proved by the pictures of "dragons" in the writing of the old scientists. Such a dragon is for instance depicted in the old book *Mundus subterraneus* of 1678, in which the learned Anastasius Kircher described the wonders of the subterranean world. The famous dragon-slayer Winkelriedt is said to have fought a life and death struggle with such a dragon at the village of Wyler in Switzerland. When we examine this creature more closely, we see that it has a long neck on a short body and that two narrow, pointed wings project from the shoulder region. If we were to attach those wings (of course with the addition of one more pair) to the dragon instead of legs and if we were to shorten its tail a little, we should get a rather successful reconstruction of the plesiosaurids. Thus it is almost certain that the original models for dragons of this type were more or less complete skeletons of plesiosaurids, discovered by chance in olden times and preserved in the castles and monasteries in their curio cabinets, where they then became known to more people than merely their disoverers. And as at that time people believed in dragons, these plesiosaur bones could be regarded as skeletons of dragons.

PL. 20

RHAMPHORHYNCHUS

In the long-ago Mesozoic era, the age of reptiles, there lived strange saurians, which in differently-shaped genera and species cleaved the boundless air; they were the so-called Pterosaurians.

They are all completely extinct; the last of them died out at the end of the Cretaceous period. All were excellently adapted to flight. Their bones were hollow (pneumatic); the fore-limbs were transformed into flight organs; a flight membrane connected the outer (fifth), unusually lengthened digit, with the body. The skull was large, elongated in front and generally pointed. The teeth, when developed, were simple and cylindrical, and grew in alveoli. The front teeth were as a rule the most powerful. The larger and stronger teeth, sometimes also curved sideways, had the function of catching the victim and holding it fast. *Ctenochasma* had the greatest number of teeth; its jaws were armed with about 360, arranged like a comb. Some pterosaurians were toothless. They lived in the Jurassic and Cretaceous. Their food consisted mainly of fish and insects.

Rhamphorhynchus is one of the best-known, and was abundant in its time. It had long, narrow, pointed wings and a large skull. The teeth were long, of irregular size, and directed forwards. The tail was unusually long and strong; it was held in an extended position, and at its end there was a perpendicular membranous lobe. Rhamphorhynchus lived only in the Upper Jurassic, and the finds of its skeletons in Bavaria are famous throughout the scientific world. There is no major museum whose collection lacks the skeleton of some Rhamphorhynchus from the Upper Jurassic of Bavaria. The largest species was *Rhamphorhynchus kokeni*, whose wing measured some 32 inches.

Outside Germany sporadic remains of rhamphorhynchuses have also been found in the Upper Jurassic at Tendaguru in Africa.

PL. 21

PTERODACTYLUS

Not only did the Rhamphorhynchuses live in the Upper Jurassic of Bavaria; so also did the flying reptiles of the genus *Pterodactylus.* They differed strikingly from Rhamphorhynchus; they had a short tail and broad wings, their skull was elongated, narrowed in front, and provided with only a few teeth. Their size differed from species to species; the smallest of them was the size of a sparrow, the largest the size of a hawk.

It is very probable that the Pterodactyli lived in large flocks on the rocks of the shore and in the woods of the Upper Jurassic sea of Bavaria. Whether they were day or night hunters cannot yet be said with certainty, but they seem to have been diurnal ones, which at dusk found safe hiding-places among the branches of the crowns of the trees or in the rock fissures, where they passed the night hanging head down, as do the bats of today.

Numerous and beautifully-preserved skeletons of Pterodactyli have been found in Bavaria. One species was also discovered in France, and unconfirmed remains come from England and from Tendaguru in Africa.

All flying reptiles of the genus Pterodactylus (and of the closely related genera *Ctenochasma* and *Gnathosaurus*) lived exclusively in the Upper Jurassic. In the Cretaceous period they were represented by other related genera (like *Ornithocheirus* from the Cretaceous of England, *Ornithostoma* from the Cretaceous of England and Russia).

It has to be emphasised that the pterosaurians were not the ancestors of the birds, as is often maintained even today. The pterosaurians represent a separate and special evolutionary branch of the reptiles, which became extinct at the end of the Cretaceous, and which have nothing to do with the birds; they sprang from entirely different reptiles.

PL. 22

PTERANODON AND TYLOSAURUS

The only true 'dragon' which in the far-off past flew in the skies of our Earth was the huge *Pteranodon*, attaining a wing-span of more than 24 ft. In the Upper Cretaceous of Kansas its remains occur so abundantly that as early as 1910, when G. F. Eaton published his outstanding monograph on them, the remains of about 465 specimens were already known.

The skull of Pteranodon was large and extended to the rear in a long bony comb. The long pointed snout was toothless and excellently adapted to the hunting of fish and molluscs. The life of Pteranodon is compared by Professor O. Abel with the life of the present-day albatross, which inhabits the open sea of the southern hemisphere. We have to regard Pteranodon as a passive flyer moving mainly in gliding flight, like the albatross, which is able to move very rapidly in the air without flapping its wings.

A very striking feature of the skeleton of the pteranodon is the relatively small size of the body proper, and connected with it is the inconsiderable size of the thorax, sacrum and pelvis. From the smallness of the last it has been correctly concluded that the female must have laid very small eggs, as it is difficult to assume viviparity among the pteranodons. At the time when the females were due to lay, they left the open sea where they usually lived, and sought dry land, just as the albatross does. Professor O. Abel assumes that, just as some sea birds select certain islands for laying their eggs, so also did the pteranodons. What a magnificent sight these 'pteranodon islands' must have presented, so different from the present-day 'bird islands'. Professor O. Abel also made the supposition that the pteranodons looked after their hatched, helpless fledglings, at least for a short time. If this was really so, then it is a phenomenon which has never occurred again among the reptiles.

The pteranodons were contemporary with the carnivorous saurians of the genus *Tylosaurus*. When hunting fish they were often scared by these savage beasts.

The Upper Cretaceous sea of Kansas has long ceased to exist; the strange 'dragons' of reality, not of fairy-tale, have long disappeared. At least 70—80 million years have passed since the time when the last pteranodon glided through the tropical air of the dying Cretaceous period.

PL. 23

BRONTOSAURUS

Brontosaurus is one of the best-known and also most discussed of giant dinosaurs. A moving mountain of flesh and bone, the brontosaurus wandered along the banks of the Jurassic swamps of North America, which were its home, and which perhaps it left only when it wished to sun itself on the sands of the shore or to lay eggs. It attained a length of about 65 ft. It had a small head, a long neck and a big, strong tail. Its brain case contained relatively the smallest brain found among the vertebrates. In addition to this brain, however, there developed in the region of the sacral vertebrae a second nerve centre, which was several times as big as the brain proper. The spinal column was composed of huge vertebrae; all were hollow, with the exception of those in the tail. Thus we have here, combined with vast dimensions, a certain saving of bony material and at the same time a lowering of the total weight of the body. The teeth were numerous and peg-shaped. The brontosauri were herbivorous, living on aquatic plants. Their body weight was great, at least some 50,000 pounds. The body probably grew very slowly; some paleontologists maintain that the brontosaurus reached an age of about 200 years.

Like the other huge herbivorous dinosaurs, they were quite helpless when attacked by the savage carnivorous saurians. Their body was not covered with any armour, and both head and body lacked bony spikes. Their best protection against predators was their mode of life. They stayed in water almost all the time; they could even feed under water, as it was sufficient for them to gulp down some air from time to time.

Brontosaurus lived in the Upper Jurassic of North America. From the bones found it proved possible to reconstruct the skeleton, which, as a precious exhibit, adorns the collections of the American Museum of Natural History in New York. Since the time that this reptilian giant inhabited our Earth at least 150 million years have passed.

PL. 24

DIPLODOCUS

In the swampy Upper Jurassic regions of present-day Wyoming and Colorado there lived another, and now quite well-known, dinosaur, *Diplodocus*. In appearance it rather resembled Brontosaurus; but it was distinguished from it by its slender, S-shaped neck and long tail, which ran out into a thin, whiplike end. It differed from Brontosaurus also in its length, which was up to 97 ft.

Diplodocus fed mainly on aquatic plants, but all kinds of small animals which lived on the plants became its prey, like insect larvae, small crustaceans, molluscs, etc.

It has been possible to examine diplodocus in great detail, mainly thanks to the munificence of Andrew Carnegie. He had large excavations made at his own expense in Wyoming, from which six skeletons were obtained; one complete skeleton made from these is today exhibited in the Pittsburgh Museum. Carnegie further had plaster casts made of this skeleton, which he donated to many European museums, as for instance the museums of Vienna, Berlin, Paris and London.

The paleontologist Hatcher, who described the skeleton of this diplodocus, called it *Diplodocus carnegii*. In addition the species *Diplodocus longus* is known, from the same regions.

Diplodocus had the same mode of life as brontosaurus—its best protection against the savage carnivorous saurians which were its contemporaries and threatened its life.

At least 150 million years have passed since the time when diplodocus inhabited our Earth.

PL. 25

BRACHIOSAURUS

Brachiosaurus is another of these huge herbivorous dinosaurs. It lived in the Upper Jurassic and Lower Cretaceous. It was of somewhat different appearance from the Brontosauri and Diplodoci. Its huge body was carried by four pillar-like limbs, of which the fore-legs were longer than the hind-legs; thus the hind part of the body seemed to be pressed down. Its long neck carried a small head, and the body ended in a short, strong tail. The species *Brachiosaurus altithorax* lived in the Upper Jurassic swamps of Colorado; its humerus measured 7 ft. *Brachiosaurus fraasi* lived in the Upper Jurassic and Lower Cretaceous swamps of Africa (Tendaguru), and its humerus measured 5 ft. 10 in.; *Brachiosaurus brancai* lived here also, and its humerus measured as much as 7 ft. 6 in., the longest humerous known.

The complete skeleton of the last species is known. It comes from the Tendaguru Beds of Africa and was excavated by the German paleontologists W. Janensch and E. Henning in 1909 and 1910. After supplementation, it was mounted and exhibited in the Geological-Paleontological Museum of Berlin University. The figures indicating the size of this skeleton are impressive; the length from mouth to end of tail is 81 ft. 8 in.; the length of the neck is 18 ft. 7 in.; the total height is 42 ft. 4½ in., the height in the area of the first thoracic vertebra is 20 ft. 9 in., and the diameter of the body is 10 ft. It should perhaps be added that this is not the skeleton of one of the largest specimens, and that scattered bones have been found which in length and thickness far exceed the corresponding bones of the skeleton measured.

The brachiosauri were able to live in much deeper waters than the brontosauri and diplodoci, as is clear from the shape of their body. The following comparison shows best how tall they were: with lifted neck they were so tall that they could leisurely and without any effort at all look in at the windows of the third storey of a house.

Not less than 100 million years have passed since the time when the last brachiosaurus perished.

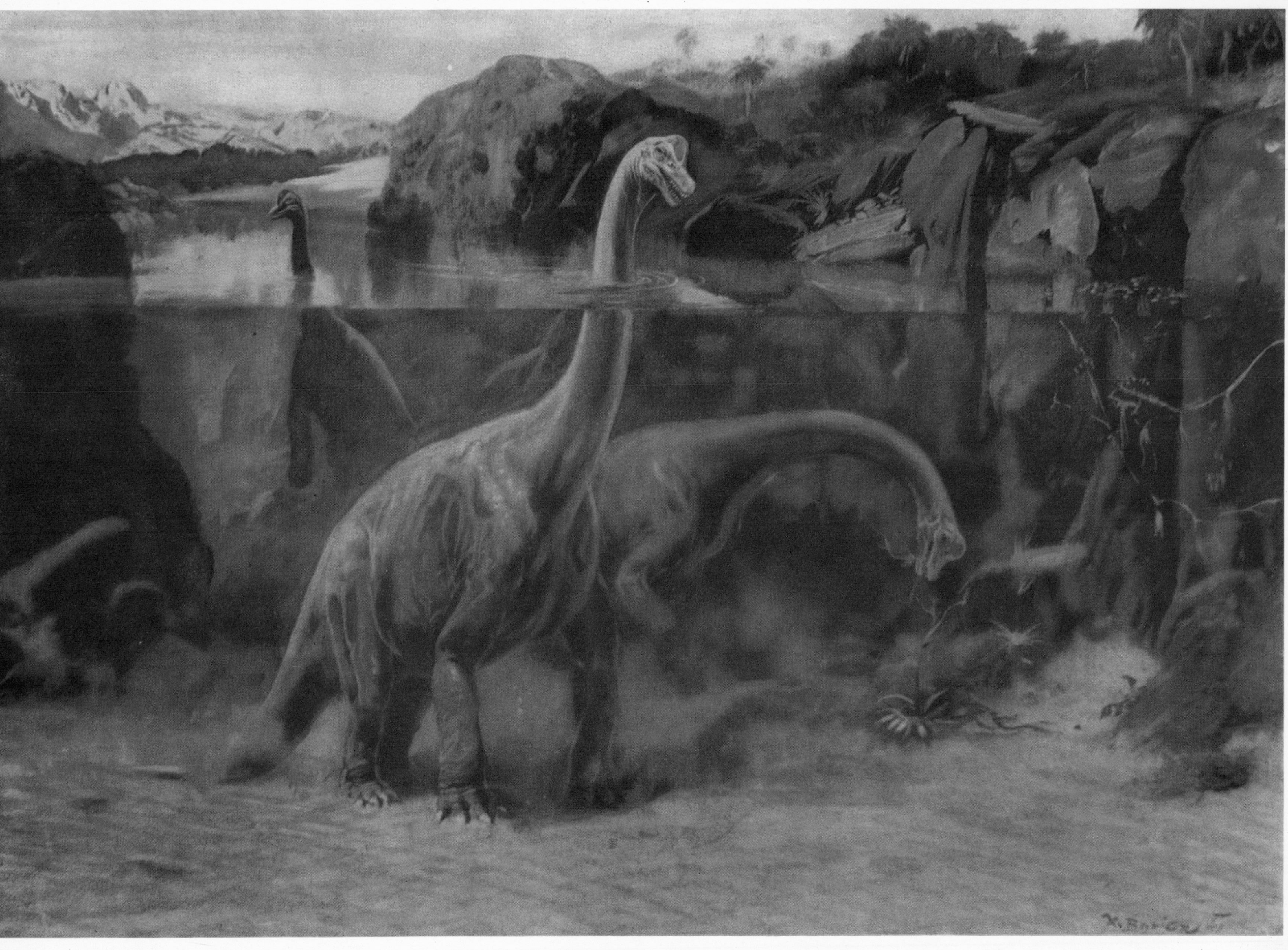

PL. 26

IGUANODON

The best known of the European finds of dinosaurs is the one made in 1877 at Bernissart in Belgium Here twenty-three more or less complete saurian skeletons were found, all belonging to the genus *Iguanodon.*

The first iguanodons were found in 1820 in England, but it was the discovery at Bernissart which showed us clearly what these saurians looked like. They were huge reptiles, 18 ft. high and 36 ft. long. They moved with a hopping gait or short gallop, using only their strong hind-legs, as the fore-legs were stunted. The elongated skull was high, and its anterior part was strongly compressed from the sides. In the jaws was a great number of flat and notched teeth with cylindrical roots. They were considerably worn by the vegetable food, and were constantly replaced by new ones. The fore-legs were much thinner and smaller than the hind-legs; they had five digits, of which the thumb was transformed into a large sharp spine which served for defence. The body ended in a long, strong tail. The iguanodontia were herbivorous, and according to L. Dolle they lived mainly on araucaria twigs, which they are said to have pulled down towards them with their long tongues (like the giraffe of today), in order to cut them off with the sharp edges of their mouths, before crushing them with their strong teeth.

Two species have been described from the locality at Bernissart, *Iguanodon bernissartensis* and *Iguanodon mantelli.* According to the Hungarian paleontologist F. v. Nopcsa these are, however, really only one species, and the different characteristics by which they are distinguished are said to be only those of sex dimorphism. Thus according to this opinion (which is, however, not generally accepted) the smaller *Iguanodon mantelli* would be the male, the larger *Iguanodon bernissartensis* the female.

In addition to these two Belgian species, we know one other species, *Iguanodon atherfieldensis,* whose skeleton was found in the lowest Cretaceous, the so-called Wealden, on the Isle of Wight.

Besides skeletons we have also numerous footprints of the iguanodontia, which they imprinted in the soft soil. These occur abundantly in the Wealden Beds of Germany and England, and are so distinct that from them we can easily tell whether they were made by a slowly walking, running or resting animal.

These iguanodontia lived in Europe about 100 million years ago.

PL. 27

STEGOSAURUS

There were also some strange dinosaurs whose body was encased in a strong hard amour, and which therefore are referred to as armoured dinosaurs. Some of them might justly be called living tanks.

Their best known and most typical representative was *Stegosaurus*, of which several species lived in the Upper Jurassic, especially in North America. The stegosauri were large reptiles; their length varied between 13 ft. and 32 ft. The huge body was carried by four limbs, of which the fore-legs were shorter than the hind-legs. The arched back carried a double row of large thick bony shields placed vertically with tips pointing upwards. They were smallest behind the head, largest above the pelvis. The short-strong tail was provided with two pairs of long bony spines. The body was covered with a strong armour composed of small horny plates. A short neck carried the small head close to the ground. The brain was so small that it was not adequate to govern the huge body; therefore the hind-legs and the powerful tail were perhaps controlled by a second nerve centre, the spinal cord being so enlarged in the region of the sacral vertebrae that the nerve substance was here ten times as voluminous as the brain proper.

The stegosauri were, however, not the only armoured dinosaurs, as there were many genera armoured in different ways. Thus for instance the Upper Jurassic *Scelidosaurus* of England, about 13 ft. long, had armour composed of longitudinal rows of bony knobs and triangular or prismatic shields; the Upper Jurassic *Kentrurosaurus*, of Africa, had its back protected by a double row of small bony shields and sharp spines; the Upper Cretaceous *Palaeoscincus* had its body covered with bony plates and its sides armed with a row of strong, sharp spines.

The stegosauri and other armoured dinosaurs were, in spite of their frightening appearance, harmless herbivores. The heavy armour did not allow them to move quickly, nor did they need to, as their strong coat of mail and their big sharp spines were a sufficient protection for them against attacks by their carnivorous contemporaries.

PL. 28

TRICERATOPS

In 1887 there was found in Colorado a pair of horn points which were submitted for identification to the famous American paleontologist O. C. Marsh. He took the horns to belong to some mammal, which he named Bison alticornis. But two years later (1889) this hypothesis was proved incorrect by the finding of a complete skull, the horns of which had the same points, and this skull was that of a reptile. This was a surprise, as until then no remains of horned reptiles had been known. The skull found was described as *Triceratops horridus*, and marked the beginning of a series of discoveries of other similar dinosaurs characterised by their skulls having a varying number of horns of different sizes and shapes. Therefore we speak of them collectively as the horned dinosaurs. Another feature which they had in common was the strange broad "neck-frill" behind the back of the skull formed by the lengthening of the parietal bones.

Triceratops is a typical representative of the horned dinosaurs; it owes its name to its very strong horns, one of which protruded upwards from the nose, the other two being sited above the eyes. It was about 20 ft. long and 8 ft. high. Its skull was more than 7 ft. long; it must of course be added that this abnormal length was due to its large neck-frill. Many species of triceratops lived in the uppermost Cretaceous of Wyoming, Montana and Colorado, in a region where there were large swamps but also higher-lying dry plateaus covered with groves of sequoias, gingkos, poplars, oaks, willows, maples and other trees, with a rich undergrowth of various shrubs and herbs.

It is interesting to note that one skull of a triceratops was found bearing the mark of an injury. One horn had been broken off at an early age. The wound, received by accident or perhaps in defence against an attacker, healed well, and the animal lived a long time after having been injured, as the normal development of the other horn indicates a great age.

Triceratops lived some 90 to 40 million years ago.

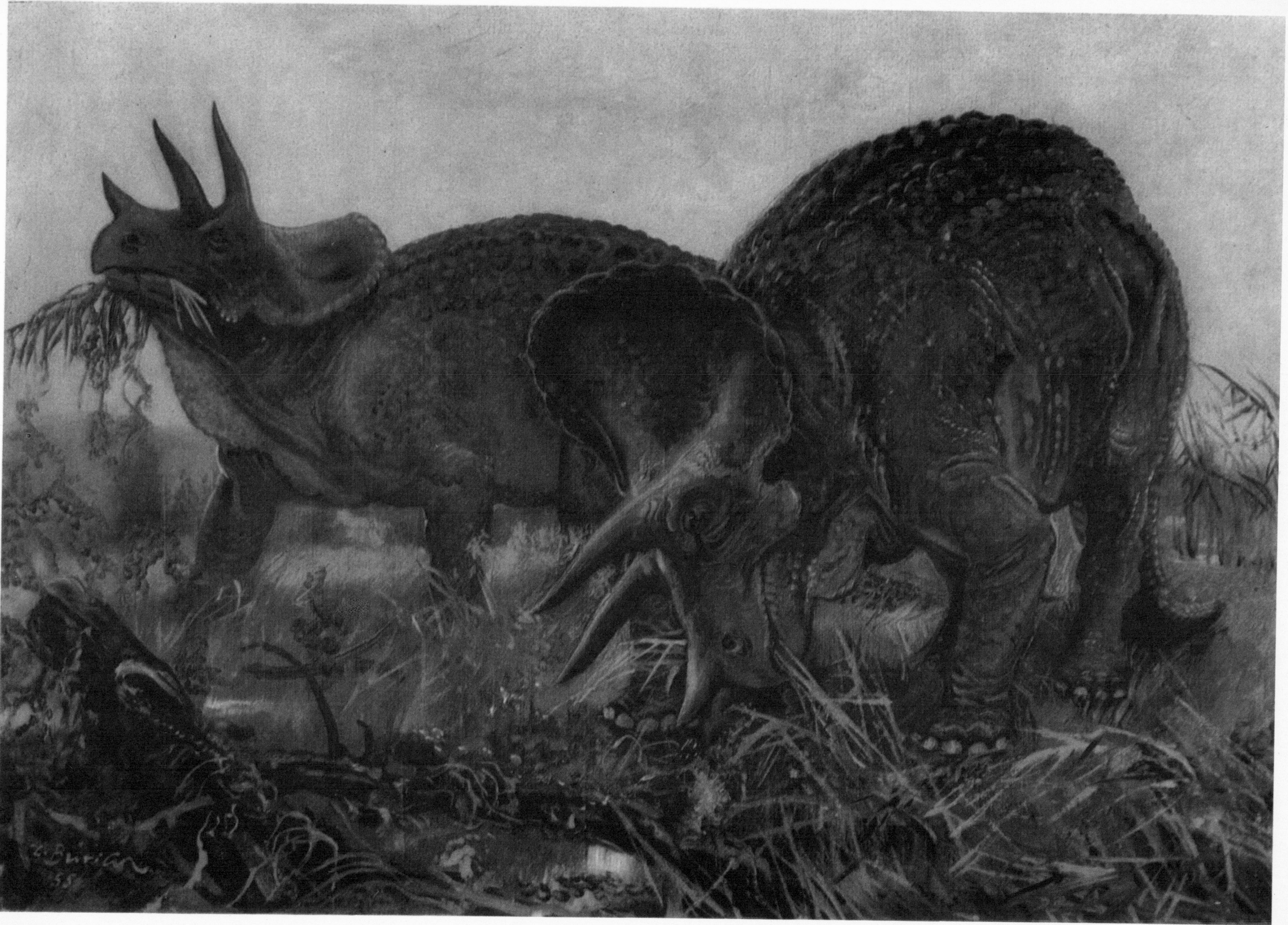

PL. 29

MONOCLONIUS

In 1914 an expedition from the American Museum of Natural History, New York, led by Barnum Brown, made an important find at Steveville in the Red Deer River basin in Alberta, Canada. The expedition discovered the complete skeleton of a horned dinosaur, which was described as *Monoclonius*. It received its name from its skull, which had only one long horn on the nose. It was over 17 ft. 6 in. long, and its skull measured 6 ft. $4^3/_4$ in. from the point of the snout to the posterior margin of the collar.

This find was important, as it enabled us to determine accurately the physical shape of one of these animals. We know today that their bodies were short, rounded, and carried by four short but strong and muscular limbs. The short neck was covered with a broad neck-frill. The tail was relatively short, and probably dragged on the ground. The eyes lay in deep sockets, and in some genera they were also protected by the rims of the horns. The teeth grew in rows, and were of the herbivorous type. From the development of the teeth, and the way in which they are worn, it may be inferred that the jaws worked like scissors; from this it follows that the vegetable food was cut rather than crushed by the teeth. The skin of all of them was thick, and was divided into a great number of irregular polygonal areas.

In addition to one complete skeleton of the genus *Monoclonius* it was possible to reconstruct from the remains of different specimens found, the skeletons of the genera *Triceratops* and *Brachyceratops*, which today stand side by side in the Natural Science Museum in Washington. A comparison of the two is very instructive: *Brachyceratops* is one of the geologically oldest genera of the horned dinosaurs and is also the smallest one (it was only 6 ft. 2 in. long and 2 ft. 8 in. high), whereas the geologically youngest *Triceratops* was the largest one (21 ft. long and 8 ft. high); this is one of the best proofs of the important paleontological law regarding increase in size in the course of phylogenetic evolution.

Monoclonius lived on our Earth some 70 to 80 million years ago.

PL. 30

STYRACOSAURUS

We know already that all the horned dinosaurs had approximately the same body shape, but that they differed greatly from each other in the number, size and position of the horns on the head. These horns either grew on the nose, as they do for instance in the modern rhinoceros, or they projected upwards from the forehead, or, though rarely, from the jugal arches. We know, however, of one whose neck-frill ran out in long sharp horns, namely *Styracosaurus*, whose skeleton was found in 1913 in the uppermost Cretaceous of the state of Alberta in Canada. The lucky finder of this monstrous beast was L. M. Lambe.

The head of Styracosaurus was armed with a nasal horn, 1 ft. 9 in. long, and the posterior margin of the perforated neck-frill was provided with six long and strong horn-like spines placed in a crescent; the head together with the collar was more than 7 ft. long and had a width of more than 5 ft. 3 in.

We know two species, *Styracosaurus albertensis* and *Styracosaurus parksi*; both were found in the same region and in layers of the same geological age (in the uppermost Cretaceous).

The strong, pointed horns of the styracosauri afforded them a good protection against the attacks of the carnivorous saurians. These generally seem to have preferred to leave adult styracosauri (and other horned dinosaurs; as for instance triceratopses and monoclonii) alone, even though hunger sometimes forced them to attack. At least the older and more experienced predators knew that an attack on a vigorous adult styracosaurus was always a gamble with death, as one clumsy movement was enough for a pointed horn, more than 1 ft. 9 in. in length, to jab into their abdomen, and with one jerk slit it from below.

But not all these dinosaurs had such formidable horns. In some types they even lost their defensive importance, and became stunted in various queer ways, as for instance in the genus *Centrosaurus*, likewise from the uppermost Cretaceous of Canada.

The skull of this relatively small genus (it was only 5 ft. long) had two short horns above the eye sockets, a short horn curved forwards above the nostrils, and finally two short, curved horns growing from the big neck-frill.

PL. 31

PROTOCERATOPS

The Central Asiatic Paleontological Expedition of the American Museum of Natural History, New York, led by the outstanding American paleontologist R. C. Andrews, worked in Mongolia and China between 1922 and 1930. The Expedition is best known to the general public for its discovery of dinosaur's eggs and embryos in the Cretaceous beds in the neighbourhood of what is now Shaberakh Usu in Mongolia. This discovery created a stir in the scientific world, as until then not one dinosaur's egg had been found, and then all of a sudden there were reports of whole nests of them found in a sandstone complex more than 200 feet thick. It was even established which dinosaur had laid these eggs. It was *Protoceratops andrewsi*, the ancestor of the North American horned dinosaurs which we have already described above.

More than seventy skulls and skeletons of Protoceratops were found near the nests. Specimens were found in all stages of growth: from the newly-hatched young to old adults. Even embryos were found in some eggs, which with their skeleton already partly ossified correspond exactly to the youngest stages of this dinosaur. These embryos are characterised by big eyes; they have a sharply-formed face lengthened into a hooked beak, and a circular neck-frill around the hind-part of the skull; in short, they already exhibit all the characteristic features of the full-grown animals, though of course in miniature.

Protoceratops lived in Mongolia in the Upper Cretaceous near the shores of a large lake. They were harmless herbivores, which reproduced by laying eggs in the sand, and according to Andrews it seems that they paid attention to the quality of the sand, avoiding that which was either too fine or too coarse.

At the same time as Protoceratops there also lived a small bipedal saurian which plundered their nests. It has therefore been called *Oviraptor*. One of its skeletons was found directly above a protoceratops' nest. We do not know what accident overtook this little thief; most probably a sandstorm buried it while it was stealing eggs.

PL. 32

CORYTHOSAURUS

If we could witness a procession of all the various dinosaurs, we should soon discover that some types which resembled each other closely in the shape of the body differed strikingly from each other in the shape of the head; and if we then excluded them from this saurian procession and placed them in a separate group, every expert would tell us that we had neatly picked out the trachodontids.

These include a great number of interesting types, distinguished from each other only by great diversity of skull shapes. The body is usually 40 ft. long, the fore-limbs are shorter than the hind ones, there are webs between the digits of the limbs, the tail is long and strong. The skin of the body is covered with polygonal, knob-shaped or conical scales. In the Upper Cretaceous their different genera and species lived all over the world; we know their remains from North America, the Netherlands, Transylvania, England, Scotland, and China. They lived in regions rich in swamps and lakes, such as their amphibian mode of life restricted them to; they always avoided desert and semi-desert areas.

Trachodon is a typical duck-billed dinosaur. It is characterised by its beak. *Corythosaurus* prided itself on its helmet-like comb, formed by some of the cranial bones (see this plate. *Stephanosaurus* was remarkable for its helmet-like comb and nasal bones elongated into tubes. *Saurolophus* had similarly lengthened nasal bones projecting far beyond the top of the head. The strangest of all of them, however, was *Parasaurolophus*. A long protuberance jutted out from its skull, which, as a cross-section shows, consisted of four tubes set close together and formed by the lengthened nasal and intermaxillary bones. It is evident that these tubes represent exceptionally-lengthened nasal passages, and when we realize that in the living animals these passages were lined with mucous membrane, we can correctly estimate their biological significance, and how greatly they increased the faculty of smell, needed perhaps in the mating season. Therefore many paleontologists believe that all trachodontids with tubular or comb-like 'ornamentations' were males, those without them females. Study of the pelvis of the different genera seems to confirm this supposition.

PL. 33

TRACHODON AND TYRANNOSAURUS

The saurian *Trachodon*, the typical representative of the trachodontids, was a very strange animal. Its skull was low and elongated and characterised by the striking likeness of its mouth to a duck-bill. The jaws of the mouth were studded with rows of teeth, more than two thousand in all. The fore-limbs were shorter than the hind-limbs. The trachodontids could walk on four legs as well as on two. The webs between their digits show that they did not live exclusively on land but in the water also. Several species of them inhabited the Upper Cretaceous of North America, and their average length was 40 feet.

Contemporary with the trachodontids and other herbivorous dinosaurs there were also carnivorous ones. One of the most terrifying of these beasts of prey was the huge *Tyrannosaurus rex*, 20 ft. high and up to 50 ft. long. Its skull was somewhat flattened on top and at the sides, and was more than 3 ft. 5 in. long; its mouth was full of large, sharp teeth. The powerful body was carried on strong hind-legs. The fore-limbs were small and stunted in growth. The body terminated in a long and powerful tail. Barnum Brown found two beautifully-preserved skeletons in northern Montana; these are today an attraction of the Museum of Natural History in New York, and are mounted as though fighting over a kill.

We know, however, not only skeletons of the tyrannosaurs but very probably their footprints also; one such found in a coal mine has a width of 2 ft. 6 in. and a length of 2 ft. 3 in.; one step of this saurian measured 13 ft. 6 in.

The appearance of a tyrannosaurus must always have struck terror into the other dinosaurs. Some of these tried to escape in the swamps (for instance the trachodontids), others fled in panic from the place of danger (as for instance the strange reptiles of the genus *Struthiomimus*, resembling ostriches minus feathers), for the enormous power of these gigantic beasts of prey could not be withstood.

PL. 34

GORGOSAURUS AND SCOLOSAURUS

The gigantic *Gorgosaurus libratus* lived in the Upper Cretaceous of Canada; it was a carnivorous reptile which attained a length of about 32 ft. In appearance it rather resembled *Tyrannosaurus*, and it was just as savage; but its stunted fore-limbs had only two digits. This colossus, whose beautifully-preserved skeleton was found on the Red Deer River in Alberta, Canada, was not able to make any sudden attacks because of its clumsiness. Thus, like *Tyrannosaurus*, it probably wandered about looking for the carcasses of herbivorous and carnivorous dinosaurs, on which to feed. It was only when some living prey crossed its path by accident that it could pounce on it and overcome it, if of course the victim did not succeed in this case also in taking to the water in the swamps or running away.

Such chance encounters certainly often took place. They were especially dangerous for various armoured saurians of smaller size, which were as ponderous as the gorgosaurians. In these cases the latter certainly attacked, and mostly with success. Such a prey might for instance be the genus *Scolosaurus*, which lived in the same region and in the same geological period as the gorgosaurians. They were about 20 ft. long, and their armour was composed of bone-plates and strong spines, of which especially big and strong ones protected the cervical and caudal part of the body. Perhaps it was enough when *Gorgosaurus*, with its powerful clawed legs, succeeded in turning *Scolosaurus* on its back, for then it could plunge its terrible toothed mouth into *Scolosaurus*'s soft abdomen, tear it open, and inflict such heavy wounds as to prevent any defensive action.

PL. 35

CERATOSAURUS AND STEGOSAURUS

Skeletal remains of a strange and savage dinosaur distinguished by a high comb on the nasal bones have been discovered in the Upper Jurassic of Colorado. It was *Ceratosaurus nasicornis*, attaining a length of 20 to 24 ft. Its fore-limbs were short, with four digits; the first and the fourth digits were, however, atrophied. It moved, like all other carnivorous saurians, only on its hind-legs, which had three toes. It had narrow plates of bone on the back around the vertebral column.

This savage saurian was not so ponderous as *Tyrannosaurus* or *Gorgosaurus*. Thus we may assume that it could also overwhelm its prey by surprise attack or catch it.

There is no doubt that on its peregrinations *Ceratosaurus* often encountered the armoured stegosauri. It is, however, probable that it did not dare to attack the adults, as this would have resulted in a life-and-death struggle. Its sharp teeth were by no means able to bite through the strong armour of the stegosauri; they rather glanced off it than tore it. It was dangerous to approach these living fortresses. One blow of their powerful tail was enough, for unless the attacker jumped back, sharp spines, 1 ft. 9 in. long, would penetrate its soft abdomen and inflict such heavy wounds that most often they proved fatal. Hence *Ceratosaurus* preferred to avoid the adult stegosauri. But it certainly attacked their young ones, as well as those of the brontosauri and other herbivorous reptiles, which it could easily overpower.

To this day we find on bones from victims of the carnivorous dinosaurs traces of the tearing off of the flesh. Long, shallow furrows on the bones are marks left by the teeth which bit greedily into the flesh of the kill and dragged and tore with brute force, regardless of the resistance of the bone.

PL. 36

COMPSOGNATHUS AND ARCHAEOPTERYX

Not all carnivorous saurians were of such immense size as those we have just described; many were, on the contrary, quite small. Among these for instance belongs *Compsognathus longipes*, whose skeletons, no larger than that of a cat, were found in the Upper Jurassic lithographic slates at Jachenhausen in Bavaria. It lived on the shore of the lagoon there, where it searched for food, also thrown up from the lagoon, and where more than once it flushed the small toothed birds of the genus *Archaeopteryx*, which lived there in its time. These birds constitute one of the best proofs of the validity and accuracy of the theory of evolution, as their skeletons bear unmistakable signs of their reptilian origin (for instance, free digits, with claws on the wings, a tail composed of twenty free vertebrae, jaws containing teeth, sclerotic rings in the eye sockets composed of many bony plates, etc.).

Archaeopteryx was only a little larger than a pigeon. It was a bad flyer; it moved mostly in parachute flight from one tree to another, or glided down to the ground, whence by means of its clawed digits it climbed up the trunk, all the way to the crowns of the trees. Archaeopteryx was not a bird of prey. Some paleontologists infer from its weak jaws studded with fine teeth that it lived on fruit and berries, while of course not despising small insects or worms either.

So far, the following remains have been found of these toothed Jurassic birds: one feather in Eichstätt (1860), an incomplete skeleton at Solenhofen (1861), a complete well-preserved skeleton at Eichstätt (1877), and a badly-preserved one at Solenhofen (1956). At first, all these four finds were included into a single genus *Archeopteryx* of two species (the feather and the Solenhofen skeleton of 1861 as *Archaeopteryx lithographica*, the Eichstätt skeleton of 1877 as *Archaeopteryx siemensi*). Later however, Bronislav Petronievié having re-examined both skeletons, came to the conclusion that they were not two species but two seperate genera; therefore, he re-named the species *Archaeopteryx siemensi* to *Archaeornis siemensi*. Gavin DeBeer of the Museum of Natural History in London did not agree with this view and considered these two species as one *(Archaeopteryx lithographica)*, saying that the small differences in the skeleton corresponded to the differences in age and sex of both individuals. De Beer's view was confirmed by F. Heller of the Erlangen University who studied the skeleton of 1956 in detail.

The first two skeletons fetched very high prices: the Solenhofen skeleton of 1861 was bought by the London museum for 14,000 marks, the Eichstätt one of 1877 by a museum in Berlin for 20,000 marks although 36,000 marks had originally been demanded for it.

Thus it was in the Upper Jurassic, approximately 150 million years ago, when the first bird's voice sounded in the tree tops. Although these were but rough cries which had no ressemblance to the beautiful songs of more recent birds, yet it was a glorious hymn announcing the arrival of a new higher type in the descent of the birds, the singers of the forests, fields and gardens.

PL. 37

HESPERORNIS AND ICHTHYORNIS

Over North America, in the region of what is now Kansas, there extended in the Cretaceous period a vast sea, inhabited by huge and savage saurians of the genera *Elasmosaurus* and *Tylosaurus*, the giant turtles of the genus Archelon, and the dragon-like flying reptiles of the genus Pteranodon. This sea was, however, also the home of the strange genera of toothed birds *Hesperornis* and *Ichthyornis*.

Hesperornis was an aquatic bird, about 3 ft. 6 in. long, whose hind-limbs were strong and adapted to swimming. All the toes were armed with claws and connected by a web. The wings were completely stunted; all that remained of them was a small humerus in the form of a thin rod. Hesperornis was thus unable to fly. On land it seems to have stood upright only very rarely; more likely it lay on the sands of the sea-shore, sunning itself after hunting for fish under the burning rays of the Cretaceous sun. Othenio Abel believes that it moved on land by raising the anterior part of its body and pushing itself off the ground by means of its legs shifted very far back; thus with small jumps it flopped ponderously forward. It was, however, an excellent swimmer, and when hunting its main food, fish, it dived with such dexterity and agility that only few escaped it. In 1870, over fifty more or less complete skeletons were found in the Cretaceous of Kansas, all belonging to the one species *Hesperornis regalis*: their discoverer was the well-known American paleontologist Professor O. C. Marsh.

Contemporaneously with *Hesperornis* there lived here also *Ichthyornis*. This was about the size of a pigeon, and was a great flier, as the well-developed wings and the high keel on the breastbone show. It too lived chiefly on fish. It occurred here in several species, of which *Ichthyornis victor* was the most abundant.

Both of these were already true birds, but still had teeth in their jaws; this was the last physical trace of their reptilian origin. The dentition was, however, different: in *Hesperornis* the teeth were set in a single groove in the jaws, in *Ichthyornis* each tooth had its own alveolus.

It seems that neither of these toothed birds lived scattered and isolated, but that they clustered together in flocks, probably very large ones of many individuals resembling the flocks of the marine birds of today in the Arctic and Antarctic regions. With the end of the Cretaceous period, about 70 million years ago, these strange toothed birds disappeared forever from the face of the earth.

PL. 38

DIATRYMA

Who does not like to remember those childhood tales in which amazing giants and dwarfs, fairies and pixies, sorcerers and witches, unicorns, basilisks and giant birds were the heroes of breathtaking adventures?

When we pass through the gallery of the ancient birds, our childhood suddenly stands up before us, suddenly the memory of those fairy-tales becomes alive. This happens when, wondering, we stand before the skeletons of two giant birds, and the poetry of the fairy-tale suddenly turns into palpable reality.

Yes, once long ago monster birds existed on our Earth. One of the first to appear was about 9 ft. high, and called *Diatryma*. It had a large skull, 1 ft. 5 in. long, with a strong beak flattened at the sides, a strong neck, and a short sturdy body with atrophied wings. The strong legs, made for running, had four toes. This bird colossus lived about 60 million years ago in the Eocene of North America. Its distant relative seems to be the modern cariama of Brazil (*Cariama cristata*), a crane belonging to the family of the Dicholophidae.

PL. 39

PHORORHACOS

Another well-known monster bird was *Phororhacos*, a huge carnivorous bird whose large skull, more than 1 ft. long, was armed with a strong, hooked beak, to this day an unmistakable sign that it was a dangerous predator, from which even quite large animals were not safe. It too was unable to fly, as its wings were weak and atrophied. Instead it ran well, as its four-toed legs were strong and powerful.

This large flightless bird lived in the Oligocene and Miocene in South America, in Patagonia. Its home was on grassy uplands or plains covered with scattered shrubs and trees.

The well-known Argentinian paleontologist Florentino Ameghino was the first to discover relics of this bird, in 1870, in Patagonia; the remains consisted of fragments of the lower jaw, which the finder assumed to belong to some edentate mammal. Only later finds convinced Ameghino that they were remains of huge birds, several species of which lived there. The best known of them is *Phororhacos inflatus*, attaining a height of about 6 ft.

Phororhacos seems to belong to the family of the Dicholophidae and to be distantly related to the present South American birds *Cariama cristata* and *Chunga burmeisteri*. It is interesting to note that together with Phororhacos there lived in these regions other similar large birds, likewise flightless, as for instance *Pelecyornis* or *Brontornis*. The view has been expressed that these giant South American birds originated towards the end of the Cretaceous or at the very beginning of the Tertiary, and that the cradle of their origin lies somewhere in the interior of Antarctica, in a region where there are today inhospitable white wastes of ice and snow, frosty gales and terrific whirlwinds, unfavourable to all living beings.

PL. 40

DINORNIS

In the Quaternary huge birds inhabited New Zealand. They were the so-called dinornithidae, known also as moa, to whose investigation the famous English paleontologist Richard Owen devoted forty-five years of his life. They were large birds, up to 13 ft. high, with a small skull and short beak, and with wings and shoulder girdle completely atrophied. In some parts of New Zealand their bones are heaped up in such quantities that they must truly be regarded as cemeteries. We know, however, not only their bones, but also mummified soft parts of their bodies, feathers and eggs. The feathers had colours which varied according to species. The eggs, likewise of different colours according to species, were large; the egg found in 1867 at Cromwell was 1 ft. long and 8 in. wide.

Several genera and species of Dinornithidae lived in New Zealand. The most characteristic and largest of them was *Dinornis maximus*, a colossus 11 ft. high.

The Dinornithidae are not related to the cassowaries or any other type of bird of the Australian animal complex. The latest investigations have shown that their closest cousins are the South American nandus (Rheae); this would be difficult to understand if we did not know from the history of our Earth that in long-ago ages New Zealand was connected with South America via Antarctica, so that the animals could migrate from one region to the other.

Man has contributed much to the extinction of the Dinornithidae. We know for certain that as late as the beginning of the sixteenth century the Maoris caught these big, clumsy birds in pits and robbed their nests of eggs. Burnt and broken bones in the kitchen-middens are the best proof that the Dinornithidae were often a Maori delicacy. To this day the Maoris maintain that their ancestors knew the bird moa well and ate its meat. Their tradition declares that the moa still lives in its retreat on the mountain Wakapunaka, and that it is guarded there by two giant lizards; it is said to be a huge bird with a human face, living exclusively on air. What a pity that this is only a myth; what a pity that here also man with his hunting and agriculture has hastened the extinction of so interesting and unusual a giant bird.

PL. 41

THE BROWN COAL FOREST

The swampy virgin forest of the Tertiary, which grew some 50 to 30 million years ago, was the source of brown coal. In many regions where there is today an active manufacturing life, and where the towers over the shafts and the slender chimneys of countless factories reach towards the sky, in the Tertiary period vast virgin forests stretched around mighty rivers, great swamps and marshes surrounded the deltas of large streams, resembling the Dismal Swamps of today on the southeastern shore of the warmer part of the United States. From the fragments of carbonised wood, and from the imprints of leaves and fruits in the clay shales which accompany the brown coal seams, we see clearly that the composition of the brown coal flora was very mixed. Here and there the coniferous *Chamaecyparis* and *Taxodium* predominated, with many aerial roots, occasionally also leafy trees like the *Nyssa*, some swamp or strongly hygrophytic oaks, maples and poplars, as well as some rather thermophytic types like magnolias. Elsewhere leafy trees predominated. Lianas, winding around the trees, gave to these brown coal forests an almost subtropical appearance, still enhanced by the presence of palms. The banks of the pools were rimmed by reeds, and their surface was covered with the leaves and flowers of various Nymphaeaceae (water-lilies). The waters were rich in fish, amphibians and reptiles; many primitive mammals made their way through the thickets, and birds flew overhead.

Our picture shows a scene from the interior of such a swamp forest with coniferous trees (*Chamaecyparis* and *Taxodium*) predominating, interspersed with some leafy trees (Nyssa). The lower parts of the trunks show how they adapted to growing in soft swampy soil. The coniferous had numerous creeping roots, the leafy trees had a markedly conical or bulbously inflated base to the trunk. In the foreground of the picture is an archaic tapir (*Palaeotapirus*) with a young one.

PL. 42

THE MIOCENE LANDSCAPE

The Tertiary, the last but one geological period in the history of our Earth is divided into an earlier section called the Paleogene and a later one called the Neogene. These two divisions differ considerably from each other in the character of their flora and fauna. Thus for instance the flora of the Paleogene very much resembles the Mesozoic flora of the Cretaceous. Palms, fig-trees, cinnamomum, acacias, myrtles, and other tropical and subtropical plants grew in profusion in Central Europe. In the Neogene, however, the appearance of the vegetation changed. The thermophile types began to retreat to the south; thus palms even now became rare in Central Europe, and deciduous forests spread considerably in the subtropical and very moist regions with their mixed growth of various oaks, beeches, maples, walnuts, sumacs, elms, plane-trees, chestnust, and other trees which today are especially common in Southern Europe and in Transcaucasia. Besides such deciduous forests, there were also coniferous ones composed of spruces, sequoias, taxodia, glyptostrobes and other trees. These, too, retreated towards the end of the Tertiary period, from Central Europe to the south, as the initial cooling of the climate was by then already a clear warning of the approach of the Quaternary and the first Ice Age.

Our picture represents part of the Miocene landscape of Central Europe, with oaks, beeches, maples and other deciduous trees, and a coniferous forest in which the tall sequoias tower above all the others. There are even some palms to remind us of the subtropical character of the region, while the fauna was likewise subtropical. The most typical members of this fauna were mastodons of the species *Trilophodon angustidens*, proboscidians with an elongated head and four distinct tusks, the first cervidae of the genus *Paleomeryx*, which were without antlers, and those of the genus *Dicrocerus*, which were the first deer to have antlers, though only quite simple ones. Whereas the mastodons had at that time already passed through a great part of their phylogenetic evolution, that of the cervidae was only just beginning.

The regions, with their virgin forests and fauna, were entirely different from those with swamps and marshes, where, as we already know, the foundations of the brown coal seams of today were laid.

PL. 43

UINTATHERIUM

The *Uintatherium* is one of the biggest and most monstrous types among the Eocene fauna of North America, a member of the extinct archaic ungulates of the order Amblypoda.

The most striking feature of the Uintatheres and of all their close relatives is the strange shape of the skull, narrowing towards the front and carrying three pairs of bony excrescences in the form of low blunt horns, which were covered with skin, as in the giraffe of today. The skull was flat and its top depressed like a dish, a feature which does not occur in any other animal. The brain was unusually small, which clearly indicates their low intelligence. Even their dentition was strange. As the intermaxillary bones were atrophied, there were no upper incisors. The lower incisors were small, and the lower canines were of the same size and shape. The upper canines were on the contrary large and sabre-shaped, slightly sharpened along the rear edge. A lobe-like expansion of the front part of the lower jaw matched the sabre-shaped canines for their whole length. These canines were more strongly developed in the males than in the females, as was the case with the horn-like excrescences on the head. For the rest the uintatheres were strangely like modern elephants.

They were herbivores, which, judging by the shape of their teeth, fed on soft and juicy plants from the swamps and rivers, not chewing them but only crushing them before swallowing.

The Dinoceratidae belong to the order of the Amblypoda, and represent the acme in that order's evolution. When we trace the phylogenetic evolution of the dinoceratids we see that their individual types begin with small forms and with little developed horn-like excrescences on the skull, and with the upper canines hardly lengthened into a sabre shape (*Bathyopsis* and *Elachoceras* of the Lower Eocene); they continue with larger forms, with these features clearly defined (*Uintatherium* of the Middle Eocene), and end with them most perfectly developed (*Loxolophodon* of the Middle Eocene and *Eobasileus* of the Upper Eocene).

PL. 44

BRONTOTHERIUM

Not only the monstrous dinoceratids (*Uintatherium*, *Loxolophodon*, etc.) lived in the Paleogene of North America, but also the strange titanotheres, huge perissodactyls, distant relatives of the present horses, rhinoceroses and tapirs, though long ago extinct. At least 50 million years have passed since the last of their representatives disappeared from the face of the Earth. Of course the titanotheres did not live only in North America, but also, though in smaller numbers, in the Paleogene of East Asia and very rarely also in Europe.

The most characteristic type of the titanotheres was *Brontotherium*, of which one species was described from a complete skeleton.

The brontotheres were big clumsy animals, larger than the largest rhinoceroses of today. Compared with their immense bodies their skulls were low and small, but very broad, which was the result of the unusual development of their zygomatic arches. The skull held a small brain, and this indicates that these giants did not distinguish themselves by their intelligence. Large bony growths, 'horns', grew from the nasal bones above the mouth, covered with skin in this case also. These horns were larger in the males than in the females. The males seem to have used them not only for defence, but also in fighting for the females. From the nature of the dentition we may infer that these giants fed on a soft and juicy vegetable diet. They lived in the lower Oligocene in grassy lowlands with many thickets and pools surrounded by mountain ridges with numerous volcanoes. From time to time the volcanoes became active, and the poisonous breath from their opened craters, and the ejected material, destroyed all life around the brontotheres.

Bones of the titanotheres have been known for a long time. They were even known to the Red Indians prior to the arrival of the first white man. Thus the Sioux, when hunting bison, found in ravines and gorges on the vast prairies of South Dakota and western Nebraska huge bones which the water had washed out during heavy downpours. As the Sioux had no idea of extinct animals, they believed that these bones belonged to the 'thunder horses', which during storms, in the flash of lightning and the noise of thunder, jump from the sky to the earth, where they hunt the bison, slaying them with their powerful hoofs. It was from this ancient Red Indian tale that Professor Marsh took the name of *Brontotherium,* or beast of thunder.

PL. 45

ARSINOITHERIUM

In 1900 Beadnell found in the Upper Eocene beds of Egypt the remains of a very strange animal, which W. C. Andrews described in detail in 1900. He called it *Arsinoitherium zitteli.* It was a huge ungulate, 11 ft. long and exceeding a stately rhinoceros in height.

The most striking feature of Arsinoitherium was its skull. Two powerful bone processes grown together at the base jutted from the nasal bones and projected above the mouth obliquely upwards in the form of huge sharp horns. They were certainly a terrible weapon, feared by even large beasts of prey. Behind them, close to their hinder edges, there grew from the frontal bones another two bony horn-like processes, but only quite small ones. In the young animal the nasal bones with their powerful 'horns' were supported by the cartilaginous nasal septum, which became ossified only in old animals. The dentition was complete; 44 teeth were set closely side by side in the jaws. All the teeth are remarkable for their archaic aspect. They had a high crown and were convex on the outside and concave on the inside. From the teeth we may infer that the food of Arsinoitherium was very similar to that of Uintatherium or the geologically old proboscidians. At present we know very little about the origin of the strange arsinoitheres, or of their relation to other animal groups. First it was thought that they were closely related to the proboscidians and the extinct ungulates of the group Amblypoda. Andrews has pointed out, however, that the arsinoitheres show a close affinity also with the Hyracoidea, which today represent a small group of ungulates mostly about the size of a rabbit, but which were generically and specifically much more abundant in the Tertiary period, and which played a fairly important role in evolution.

The Arsinoitheres lived in Egypt some 50 million years ago; as suddenly as they appeared they became extinct. Only their skeletons prove today that they ever existed.

PL. 46

DEINOTHERIUM

Deinotherium (formerly called *Dinotherium*) is a strange Tertiary proboscidian, whose most characteristic feature was that the anterior part of the lower jaw turned downwards almost in a right angle and carried a pair of large, down-curved and pointed tusks, the transformed second incisors. For the rest the deinotheres resembled the elephants of today.

Remains of the deinotheres have long been known. They were not, however, regarded from the beginning as belonging to ancient proboscidians; the earlier paleontologists (setting aside the fantastic supposition that they were the skeletons of giants) identified the incomplete remains as the teeth and bones of tapirs, hippopotami, or even of aquatic mammals. It was not until 1832 that the find of a whole skull at Eppelsheim in the Rhineland enabled Kaup and Klipstein to class the deinotherium definitely with the proboscidians. This correct placing of the deinotherium in the animal system was later fully confirmed by the Czechoslovak finds, of the bones of two adult specimens at Opatov near Česká Třebová in 1853 and of a complete skeleton at Františkovy Lázně in 1883.

The deinotheres belong to a separate family, now long extinct, of the proboscidians. Very little is known about their origin. They evolved in the Paleogene of India or Africa. In Europe they first appeared in the Lower and Middle Miocene (the smaller *Deinotherium bavaricum* and the larger *Deinotherium levius*), and died out in the Pliocene, at the very end of the Tertiary period, with the species *Deinotherium giganteum*. The biggest specimen, described as *Deinotherium gigantissimum*, was found in 1890 in the Middle Pliocene at Mazanti in Roumania; it seems, however, to be only a huge, very old male of the species *Deinotherium giganteum*.

The deinotheres inhabited fairly moist regions with swamps and a rich vegetation, which still included a great number of thermophile types such as palms, cinnamon-trees, laurel-trees and others.

PL. 47

INDRICOTHERIUM

In the Middle Oligocene, when the broad arm of the sea connecting the Caspian Sea with the Arctic sea broke up into a great number of independent water basins, large areas of Kazakhstan were covered by shady forests composed of beeches, hornbeams, walnut-trees, liquidambars and sequoias. These forests bordering the water basins and the sluggishly-flowing streams alternated with dense thickets of shrubs and swampy and marshy areas where grew a luxuriant vegetation; and everywhere there lived a rich fauna: in the forests the strange long-claws ungulate *Schizotherium*, in the thickets and swamps *Anthracotherium*, an artiodactyl resembling the pig, small deer without antlers, and other animals. But besides these moist regions there developed also vast dry grassy regions sparsely dotted with trees. It was in these areas that *Indricotherium*, a gigantic rhinoceros, lived. It had no horns and looked quite unlike a rhinoceros: it was 17 ft. high and among the biggest land mammals which ever lived on our Earth. It wandered about in small herds, and lived mainly on the leaves of the trees whose crowns it could easily reach. Remains of its skeletons have been found in southern Kazakhstan and on the shores of the Aral Sea.

The closest relative of this mammalian monster lived in Baluchistan and in Mongolia. It was *Baluchitherium grangeri*, 28 ft. long and 18 ft. high. This hornless rhinoceros was perhaps the largest of all land mammals. We can perhaps best form an idea of its size by a comparison: the Indian rhinoceros would reach about two-thirds of the way up Baluchitherium's fore-limbs, and a man, 6 ft. 2 in. tall, to the same height; a column of soldiers six abreast could pass under its belly as easily as under a triumphal arch.

The indricotheres and baluchitheres represent the oldest rhinoceros type from the evolutionary viewpoint, which after a short flowering at the end of the Lower Tertiary suddenly became extinct.

PL. 48

MEGATHERIUM

In 1789 the skeleton of a huge animal was found in the loess of the pampa near Buenos Aires, and was sent shortly afterwards to Madrid, where Joseph Garriga studied it thoroughly for several years. When he had finished his work, he sent his manuscript to the printers. That was in 1795. When Garriga received the first proofs, an unfortunate incident took place. The governor of the French colony of San Domingo visited him, and asked for a copy of the proofs, which also contained a picture of the reconstruction he had made of this animal. Garriga let him have a copy without misgivings. The governor did not, however, keep it, but sent it at once to the Academy of Science in Paris. And thus it came about that at the next meeting of the Academy the celebrated Cuvier gave a report on this skeleton, which he called *Megatherium americanum.* Thus he preceded Garriga's communication by a whole year, as the work of the latter appeared only in 1796.

The Megatherium, the great beast as we might translate its Greek name, attained a length of over 24 ft., and in height it exceeded even the largest elephants. It was a ponderous, slow and stupid animal, with a low and narrow skull and a small brain. The long body ended in an unusually thick tail. The hind-legs were strong and very sturdy; the fore-legs were a little lighter. It is noteworthy that in walking the animal did not touch the ground with the whole of the soles, but only with their edge. Of the teeth only the molars were developed, being high and four-edged. Thought the megatheres were very heavy animals, they were able to stand on their hind-legs, supporting themselves with their fore-legs on a trunk or the strong branch of a tree, and munching the young leaves they could reach in this way. Of course the leaves of shrubs and trees were not their only food. They did not disdain grasses, and sometimes they may also have dug up, with their sharp claws, tasty and fleshy onions and bulbs of various plants.

Various species of the megatheres, which belong to the mammalian order of the edentates, lived in the Pleistocene of South America. When North and South America became connected by a land-bridge, the megatheres migrated into North American regions also, where their skeletons have been found.

PL. 49

NOTHROTHERIUM

In 1928 a noteworthy discovery was made in a lava fissure in Dona Ana County, New Mexico, near El Paso in Texas. At a depth of about 100 ft. there was found the skeleton of a Pleistocene edentate mammal of the genus *Nothrotherium*. The skeleton was complete, and all its bones were still connected by tendons. Even fragments of the skin and muscles had been preserved, as well as powerful claws on the feet. The body had been naturally mummified in the dry air and constant high temperature; for the paleontologists, this is welcome, as it preserves not only the hard parts of the body (bones, teeth, etc.) but also the horny claws, pieces of the skin, muscles and other soft parts. With the skeleton of the animal were found also its faeces, containing remnants of the vegetable food last eaten.

How did the skeleton of this edentate get into such a strange place? It can be explained only by the animal having fallen into the fissure, which was 10 ft. wide at the top, reaching down almost vertically to a depth of 100 ft. It cannot have been a hiding-place, as any animal wanting to enter it would have fallen down. It seems to have been an accident which caused the fall of the megatherium. It may have been due to the carelessness of the animal itself, but it may also have happened when this harmless herbivore saw some predator approaching, for instance the sabre-toothed smilodon. Overcome by terror, perhaps, it fled helterskelter and fell into the fissure. Nor need this have happened in flight. It would have been enough if it had been browsing nearby and suddenly found itself confronted by the beast of prey; a few terrified steps back would have brought it to the rim of the fissure, which would have broken under its great weight, and fallen with the animal into the depth. Our picture tries to illustrate this suggested cause of the death of the nothrotherium, even though we cannot and indeed do not wish to maintain that it really happened in this way.

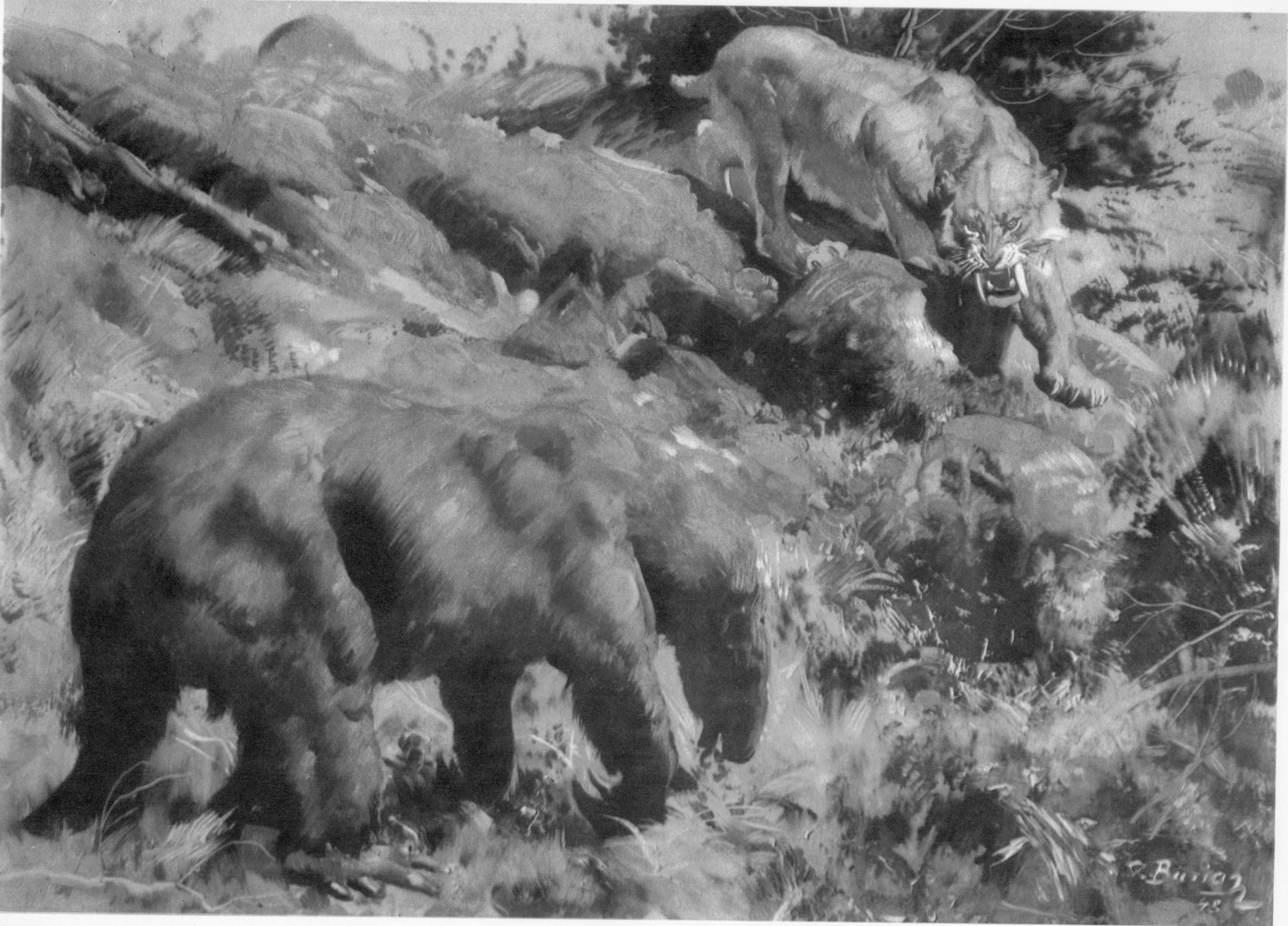

PL. 50

MAMMOTH

The mammoth (*Mammonteus primigenius*) is the best known and most representative Pleistocene animal. It was a huge proboscidian, attaining in Europe an average height of about 12 ft. Its body was covered with long dense hair which, together with a thick layer of fat under the skin, protected it against the severe climate of the Ice Age. The head was large, more powerful than in the elephants of today; this is connected with the unusually strongly developed tusks, which were recurved. They are two transformed upper jaw incisors. The molars (four in number) were high and large. The ears were small, covered with hair. The mammoths had a large hump on the back; it was perhaps a hump of fat on which they lived when the snow storms of the bitter winters buried the poor vegetation of the tundras and steppes under snow drifts. The tail was short and covered with matted hair. The trunk, too, was covered with hair. The end of the trunk was different from that of the present elephants, as the upper lip was developed so as to resemble a broadly finger-shaped outgrowth; the lower lip formed a lobe.

The mammoths were the typical inhabitants of the tundras and steppes. In their cadavers, preserved in the frozen soil of Siberia, often even the contents of the stomach have been found, from which it is ascertained that the mammoths lived on the twigs of various coniferous trees as well as on those of willows, birches and elms, and that they also ate various steppe plants.

The mammoths, contemporaries of early man, had an unusually large area of distribution. With the exception of the Spanish and Greek peninsulas, they are known throughout the whole of the continent of Europe, from which they spread via northern Asia to North America, using the then existing land-bridge between the two continents. Thus their remains have been found in many countries. In Czechoslovakia it is Moravia which is exceptionally famous for the finds of mammoth bones; Předmostí, near Přerov, and Dolní Věstonice, near Mikulov, are among the most important localities. In Siberia, however, we find in the frozen soil and ice complete mammoth bodies, which local people search for to get the valuable tusks. Complete mammoth skeletons are nothing rare in the large museums. The museum of the Academy of Science in Leningrad has, however, an exhibit unique in the world, a stuffed mammoth, whose body was discovered in 1907 in Siberia in the bank of the river Berezovka, and which a special expedition saved from destruction.

PL. 51

WOOLLY RHINOCEROS

The large woolly rhinoceros *Coelodonta antiquitatis* was a constant and faithful companion of the mammoth, that most characteristic animal of the Ice Age. The woolly rhinoceros was covered with coarse hair, and inhabited the cold tundras and steppes. It was a huge animal; it attained a length of about 12 ft. and a height of 6 ft. The skull was provided with horns set one behind the other, of which the anterior one attained a considerable length (up to 3 ft. 6 in.) and a great thickness in old males. These horns not only served the animals as an excellent defence against attacks of various beasts of prey, but were also a good offensive weapon. They have been known for a long time, and it is not without interest that the Siberians, as Pfizenmeyer pointed out, regarded them as remains of a huge fairy-tale bird, which they called 'Griffin'. Until recently the Siberian natives searched for them assiduously, the Chinese regarded them as an important medicinal drug for which they paid well. The food of the woolly rhinoceros was the same as that of the mammoth. In Siberia remains of food have been found between their teeth, chiefly bits of twigs of coniferous trees and willow leaves. Especially in winter the woolly rhinoceros was restricted to this food; in summer, when the tundra or steppe was not covered with a thick layer of snow, its bill of fare was varied by herbs and grasses.

We know particularly well how the woolly rhinoceros looked, as not only have skeletons been found in great numbers in many European countries, but bodies, too, have been excavated from the frozen soil and ice of Siberia and from the salt clays at Starun in Galicia. We even posses paintings and petroglyphs by Pleistocene artists, often beautifully executed, which tell us of the appearance of these interesting animals (and of the mammoths likewise).

The woolly rhinoceros, like the mammoth, was contemporary with prehistoric man, who hunted and ate it. But he did not just go out to meet it in open fight, using instead various cunning ruses in hunting it.

PL. 52

GIANT ELK

The giant elk (*Cervus megaceros*) is unquestionably one of the most magnificent antler-bearing animals which has ever lived on our Earth. It belongs to the Pleistocene, and had a considerable distribution throughout Europe and adjoining regions. It was a strong and heavy beast with imposing antlers which had a span of up to 11 ft. As they somewhat resembled those of the present-day fallow-buck, the giant elk was formerly regarded as one of these and therefore incorrectly called a giant buck. It lived on the broad open plains which were covered with grasses and shrubs. It avoided the forests because of the huge span of its antlers.

Several races of these giant elks lived during the Pleistocene in Europe. When we trace the development of their antlers, we see that in the course of time they became more and more weighty and larger and larger, their upper end grew more and more like a shovel in shape, and the number of branches constantly increased. The lowest one, the brow-antler, underwent the most important change, as in the geologically youngest species (*Cervus megaceros hibernicus*) it spread into the shape of a spoon or branched into two. The antlers, which adorned only the head of the males, were heavy; the weight of one amounted to as much as 72 lbs.

The giant elks had a considerable geographical distribution. To the south they spread as far as to northern Italy and southern France, to the west to Ireland, to the north via Denmark to Siberia, where many bones have been found so beautifully preserved that they look like bones of today, and to the east as far as to the Altai. But throughout the whole of this vast area they always belonged among the rather rare animals.

The giant elk was a contemporary of man. But the ancient hunters hunted it little, perhaps only when a specially favourable opportunity offered itself. We may infer this from the fact that bones of this stag are always very rare in the kitchen-middens.

A pity, a thousand pities, that this magnificient antler-bearer has become completely extinct.

PL. 53

EOHIPPUS

As we know the evolution of life as a whole, so also we know the evolution of its individual groups or types. Though we do not yet understand all its details and causes, even here the paleontologists have accomplished much and have proved many facts convincingly. One of he most impressive examples of their work is the tracing of the ancient history of the evolution of the horse, that noble animal and helper of man in his work. This, which began some 50 million years ago and which in North America formed the evolutionary series *Eohippus – Orohippus – Epihippus – Mesohippus – Miohippus – Parahippus – Merychippus – Pliohippus* – true horse (*Equus*), is the most striking example of the relation of organisms to their environment; it is a proof that changes in the environment forced the organisms to pass through corresponding changes which enabled them to survive. In the ancient history of the evolution of the horse the alterations in the environment which had the greatest effect on the horse were the change from swampy and marshy regions to drier steppe regions and the difference in the quality of the food closely connected with this, especially the transition from soft and juicy swamp plants to hard and dry steppe grasses. Below we shall introduce you to some members of this evolutionary series of the horse in North America.

The North American series of horses begins with a small creature of the genus *Eohippus*, which lived in the swamp regions of the virgin forests of the Lower Eocene. It was about as large as a fox. The small head was set on a short neck and the body with its arched back was carried on relatively long legs, of which the fore-limbs had five toes, the hind-limbs three. But of the five toes on the front feet only four had hoofs, the fifth being atrophied and displaced upwards, and no longer touching the ground. On the hind legs all three were provided with tiny hoofs, but the two lateral digits had long been atrophied, and in the form of small bones displaced high up on the back of the foot they were hidden under the skin. There were still 46 teeth in the mouth; the molars were small, with a low crown adapted to crush the soft and juicy vegetable food. The ulna and fibula, which in the further course of evolution became more and more atrophied, were in eohippus still distinctly developed. The tiny eohippus was the first true archaic horse to appear on our Earth. From it we can trace an uninterrupted series of successors leading to the modern horse. We know some ten species of eohippus, varying in size; the height of the smallest (*Eohippus index*) was only 10 inches, the height of the largest (*Eohippus resartus*) was about 1 ft. 6 in.

PL. 54

OROHIPPUS

The first successor of Eohippus in the North American series of horses was *Orohippus*. It lived in the Middle Eocene, but also somewhat differently and in other regions than Eohippus. Its remains have been found in what is now Bridger Basin in Wyoming.

In appearance *Orohippus* still greatly resembled Eohippus, nor did it differ much from it in size. The species *Orohippus osbornianus* was only 1 ft. 3 in. high at the shoulder. The skull, which was not longer than that of a dog, was already of markedly equine appearance; only the eye sockets lay further forward. The fore-limbs had four toes. The metacarpus and metatarsus, which together may be called the metapodia, were more strongly developed in the middle digit in than the two lateral digits. The two lateral digits of the hind-legs had already become so atrophied in *Eohippus* that only tiny bones remained of them, and they disappeared completely in *Orohippus*. The back was still moderately arched. The most important change which took place in the teeth was that the upper premolars (the third, and especially the fourth) began to assume the unmistakable shape of molars; there was a transition from the triangular shape characteristic for Eohippus, to a square shape.

The region of the Bridger Basin of today was at that time a swampy area with numerous lakes and a rich vegetation. Here and there bogs formed, from which later small brown coal deposits were to develop. Many rivers flowed through the region and they, like the small lakes and pools, were rich in fish. Many crocodiles inhabited the rivers, lakes and pools, and various mud-turtles lived near them. Besides the swamps and marshes there were also broad bands of dry and shrubby steppe. *Orohippus* did not live in swamp forests as *Eohippus* had done, but selected for its home the drier grassy and shrubby plain. *Epihippus*, the early horse and successor of *Orohippus* in the Upper Eocene, also had its home in a similar region.

PL. 55

MESOHIPPUS

Thousands and thousands of years passed and the land changed. Where before there had been swamps, there now stretched wide grassy plains. On the banks of the rivers, which from time to time flooded the land, great elms and many shrubs grew luxuriantly, whereas the dry soil of the grassy plains supported only various kinds of thorn-bushes. The vast primeval forests with swamps and marshes had gone. So it was too in the region of Little Bad Land in the present Nebraska and the Big Land in what is now South Dakota when the sun of the Lower Oligocene shone on our Earth. These endless grassy plains became the home of the small horses of the genus *Mesohippus*. These can no longer be called archaic horses, as they lived at the beginning of the second section of the North American series of the horses, of that section which leads directly to the modern horse.

In the Lower Oligocene *Mesohippus* lived in large herds in present-day Nebraska and South Dakota. They were about as large as the wolves of today, and were divided into several species. They walked on three digits of all four feet; the middle digit was distinctly longer and stronger than the two lateral ones, and carried most of the weight of the body. The molars of mesohippus were still, as in the early horses, without cement, and distinctly show that it already lived exclusively on a vegetable diet, which had not always been the case with the early horses. Mesohippus clearly represents a higher stage of development than epihippus. This is especially shown by the striking morphological change of all upper premolars, which assumed the shape of molars, and in the development of the limbs, which became still more capable of running on hard, dry soil. Mesohippus was the first horse which by its movement, quick run and trot, evinced the first stage of the movement of the modern horse. This is the result of the change of environment from the original swamp forests rimming the foot of the mountains to wide dry grassy plains. The most abundant species was *Mesohippus bairdii*, with a shoulder height of about 2 ft.

In the Upper Oligocene mesohippus was replaced by *Miohippus*, whose direct descendant was the Lower Miocene *Parahippus*. In these small horses the changes in the teeth and limbs were still more accentuated. Parahippus, which lived throughout the grassy plains from the present Montana to Texas, exhibited still another modern feature in its teeth, as cement appeared on their crowns and outer sides.

PL. 56

MERYCHIPPUS

Merychippus developed from *Parahippus* some time towards the end of the Lower Miocene. It lived from the Middle Miocene to the Pliocene in present-day Nebraska. Progress was here again especially marked in the teeth (more abundant formation of cement, lengthening of the crowns of the permanent teeth) as well as in the limbs (the ulna and radius, like the fibula and tibia, became a miniature replica of these bones in the modern horse; the lateral digits were displaced so high up that even their hoofs did not touch the ground).

At the boundary between the Lower and Middle Miocene there was a great expansion of these archaic tridactyle horses, whose size varied between that of a calf and that of a donkey. We know of some twenty-five different species. The most important of these species evolutionally is that of *Merychippus primus*. This not only forms the link with the Upper Miocene species, *Merychippus paniensis*, but is also the starting-point for two independent evolutionary branches, one of which led to the origin of the genus *Hipparion* and related types known from the Upper Miocene and Pliocene of North America, Asia, Africa, and Europe, while the other lead via the Upper Miocene genus *Protohippus* to the Pliocene genus *Pliohippus* and from this straight to the genus *Equus* (horse).

Besides the North American centre of evolution of the horse there was another centre in Europe, but the latter is not nearly so important as the North American one; the series of its types being far poorer and less complete. The first European horses appeared in the Lower Eocene, just as in North America; but the last member of the European series of horses became extinct as early as the Lower Oligocene.

Thus only the North American series of evolution is of importance for the origin of the true horse (*Equus*), as it alone proceeded from the primitive Lower Eocene horse of the genus *Eohippus* through a number of gradually-modified links, more and more perfect and specialised, to the final type, the type of the true horse (*Equus*). Thus the horse originated in North America, where its main evolution also took place. But it came about that at the end of the Pleistocene all horses became completely extinct in North America. We do not yet know what was the cause. It is, however, certain that there were no horses there at the time of the arrival of the first Europeans, i.e. towards the end of the fifteenth century, nor had the natives any name for them. Thus the Old World gave to the New World a most precious gift—the horse. It gave it the animal which had its earliest home on that continent, which had developed there for many hundreds of thousands of years, and which had then in its final, culminating form crossed the still existing land bridge into Asia and thence into Europe, where it developed further and whence it then (long after its last relative in America had died out) returned to its original home, there to become the friend of man and his helper in his work.

PL. 57

MACHAIRODUS

In the older Quaternary, in the Pleistocene, there lived in Europe a large beast of prey, perhaps the one best armed to kill. It was *Machairodus*. It belonged to the cat-like predators (Felidae), though not to the true cats (Felinae), which include for instance the lion and the tiger (which it very much resembles), but to the extinct sabre-toothed carnivores (Machairodontinae). Although both these branches of cat-like carnivores had the same ancestors, yet their respective phylogenetic evolutions proceeded from the very beginning quite separately and independently. Whereas in the true cats the upper canines became smaller and smaller, in the course of evolution they increased in size in the sabre-toothed carnivores. This culminated in the Pleistocene species *Machairodus latidens*, in which the sabre-shaped canines, slightly flattened and sharpened along the rear edge, grew to a length of about 6 inches, while their roots penetrated the upper jaw so far that they reached to the upper edge of the eye sockets. When the mouth was closed these most murderous weapons projected far outside, but to use them the beast had to open its mouth wide, which it was able to do thanks to the special way in which the lower jaw was attached to the skull.

The history of the evolution of these prehistoric sabre-toothed carnivores can be traced to the Upper Tertiary in Europe, Asia and North Africa, i.e. to the time of their greatest expansion. In the beginning of the Pleistocene they attained, however, their greatest degree of specialisation, and soon afterwards they became completely extinct. *Machairodus zwierzyckii* is one of the oldest Pleistocene types; its skeletal remains were found in Java in the same strata as the remains of the ape-man of Java (*Pithecanthropus erectus*): this is an unmistakable sign that this ape-man, living about 600,000 years ago, more than once fled in terror from this carnivore.

There is no doubt that these sabre-toothed carnivores caused fear and alarm wherever they appeared. They hunted chiefly gazelles, antelopes, and the extinct small tridactyle horses of the genus *Hipparion*, while in the opinion of some paleontologists they did not hesitate to attack even the large proboscidians and rhinoceroses.

PL. 58

SMILODON

Sabre-toothed carnivores, whose evolutionary history we can trace back to the Lower Tertiary, also lived in North and South America. The best known American sabre-toothed carnivore is the Pleistocene *Smilodon*, complete skeletons of which were found in California and the Argentine.

The Californian locality at Rancho-la-Brea near Los Angeles is especially important. In the Pleistocene there was a great lake there set in the midst of a wide steppe country, and from far and near the animals came to it to slake their thirst; but its shores were rimmed by a sticky mass of asphalt. This often trapped the unwary animals, which became literally glued to it, and were then an easy prey for various carnivores, including the smilodons. Of course the older and more experienced smilodons (of the species *Smilodon californicus*) did not hunt such a prey, for they knew that they might come to grief in the treacherous asphalt. Therefore the smilodon skeletons from this locality are almost exclusively those of young, inexperienced animals, which let themselves be lured on to the asphalt by easy prey. Such a fate overtook the one in our picture, which rashly threw itself on a young archaic elephant of the genus *Archidiscodon* that had become stuck in the pitch-pool on its way to the drinking-place.

The Argentinian species *Smilodon neoganeus*, whose skeletons occur abundantly in the Pleistocene loams of the vast pampas, is largely responsible for the extinction of many large South American mammals, especially edentates. Though like all other American representatives of the genus Smilodon it originated on the soil of the northern continent, yet it invaded South America across the land bridge between the two, carrying with it the destruction of many South American animals.

PL. 59

CAVE BEAR

The cave bear (*Ursus spelaeus*) was the most powerful beast of prey of the European Pleistocene. It was a good third larger and stronger than its present relative, the brown bear (*Ursus arctos*). The front half of its body was more powerfully built and also higher than the hind part. The surface profile of the skull of the cave bear, when compared with that of the brown bear, is striking, especially for its steeply-inclined forehead. The cave bear was neither a true carnivore nor an omnivore, but lived almost exclusively on vegetable food, in contrast to its carnivorous ancestors. Soft and also hard plants and fruits served it as food, as is indicated by its considerably worn teeth. The females had one or two cubs and chose suitable corners of caves for bringing them forth, especially where a spring of clear water issued from the fissures of the limestone walls. The proximity of water was an advantage for the female, as she then did not have to leave her young ones for any length of time in order to replace by drinking the loss of water in her body, caused by suckling her cubs.

The cave bear, too, was a contemporary of man. It was of great importance for Neanderthal man (*Homo primigenius*) of Europe and it was the chief animal he hunted. Thus we need not wonder that it was also the object of the oldest human magic hunting cults, the so-called bear cults, whose traces have recently been found in some Alpine caves. The later prehistoric hunters (*Homo sapiens fossilis*) regarded the cave bear as the most desirable prey.

Bones of cave bears occur very abundantly in the caves of Europe. Some caves in Moravia and Slovakia have become famous for such finds. Many tales of dragons and monsters were certainly inspired by old finds of bones and skulls of cave bears sticking out of the loam of dark and gloomy cave galleries. Some learned medieval works, indeed, incorrectly describe and depict skulls and bones of cave bears as remain of dragons, so we can see that the dragons of our fairy-tales may have very different ancestors.

PL. 60

The authors wish to express their thanks to the following departments and institutions for permission to reproduce some of the pictures in their possession: Ministry of Culture, Prague (pls. 5, 6, 7, 14, 25, and 43), State Educational Publishers, Prague (pls. 1, 2, 24, 54, 55, 56, and 57), and Silesian Museum, Opava (pls. 38, 39, and 41). Professor František Němejc co-operated with us in the production of pls. 5, 6, 14, and 42, and Docent Ferdinand Prantl in the production of pls. 1 and 2. The remaining plates have either been reproduced from books by one of the authors (Professor Josef Augusta) or have been prepared specifically for the present work.